ST(P) MATHEMATICS 2B

ST(P) MATHEMATICS series

ST(P) 1A
ST(P) 1B
ST(P) 1A Teacher's Notes and Answers
ST(P) 1B Teacher's Notes and Answers

ST(P) 2A
ST(P) 2B
ST(P) 2A Teacher's Notes and Answers
ST(P) 2B Teacher's Notes and Answers

ST(P) 3A
ST(P) 3B
ST(P) 3A Teacher's Notes and Answers
ST(P) 3B Teacher's Notes and Answers

ST(P) 4A
ST(P) 4B
ST(P) 4A Teacher's Notes and Answers
ST(P) 4B Teacher's Notes and Answers

ST(P) 5A (with answers)
ST(P) 5B (with answers)

ST(P) 5C
ST(P) 5C Copy Masters
ST(P) 5C Teacher's Notes and Answers

ST(P) Resource Book

ST(P) Workbooks:
Drawing and Using Curved Graphs
Measuring Instruments
Symmetry and Transformation
Straight Line Graphs

ST(P)
MATHEMATICS 2B

L. Bostock, B.Sc.

S. Chandler, B.Sc.

A. Shepherd, B.Sc.

E. Smith, M.Sc.

Stanley Thornes (Publishers) Ltd

First published in 1990 by:
Stanley Thornes (Publishers) Ltd
Old Station Drive
Leckhampton
CHELTENHAM GL53 0DN
England

Reprinted 1991

British Library Cataloguing in Publication Data

ST(P) mathematics
   2B
   1. Mathematics
   510

   ISBN 0-7487-0144-3

Typeset by Tech-Set. Gateshead. Tyne & Wear.
Printed and bound in Great Britain at The Bath Press. Avon.

CONTENTS

vii

INTRODUCTION

This is the second book in a series designed for use in secondary schools and it is intended to be used in the second year (year 8) for pupils working at about Level 4/5 of the National Curriculum.

Together with books 1B and 3B, the series aims to prepare pupils to achieve at about Level 6 for the tests at the age of 14 plus (i.e. Key Stage 3, at the end of year 9). Books 4B and 5B continue the work necessary to achieve the intermediate levels at GCSE.

There are plenty of straightforward exercises, with questions divided into two types.

The first type, identified by plain numbers, e.g. **12.**, helps you to see if you understand the work. These questions are considered necessary for every chapter you attempt.

The second type, identified by a single underline, e.g. **12.**, are extra, but not harder, questions for quicker workers, for extra practice or for later revision.

Most chapters end with mixed exercises. These will help you revise what you have done, either when you have finished the chapter or at a later date.

Finally a word of advice: when you arrive at an answer, whether with the help of a calculator or not, always ask yourself 'Is my answer a reasonable one for the question that was asked?'

1 DECISION TREES

The manager of a garden centre found that the customers had mixed up all his daffodil and tulip bulbs. There were two sizes of each kind of bulb, standard and giant.

I'D BETTER SORT THEM OUT IN TWO STAGES.

FIRST I'LL SEPARATE THE DAFFODIL BULBS FROM THE TULIP BULBS.

THEN I'LL SORT THE STANDARD BULBS FROM THE GIANT SIZE.

Doing the sorting this way, the manager did not have too many choices to think about all at once.

We can describe his method by using a *decision tree*.

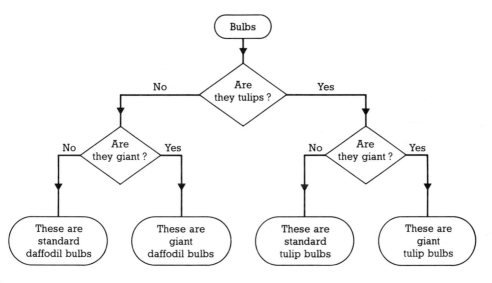

1

Whenever we have to sort a set of objects which differ in a number of ways it is usually better to use a system like the one on page 1 and to do the sorting in stages.

EXERCISE 1a

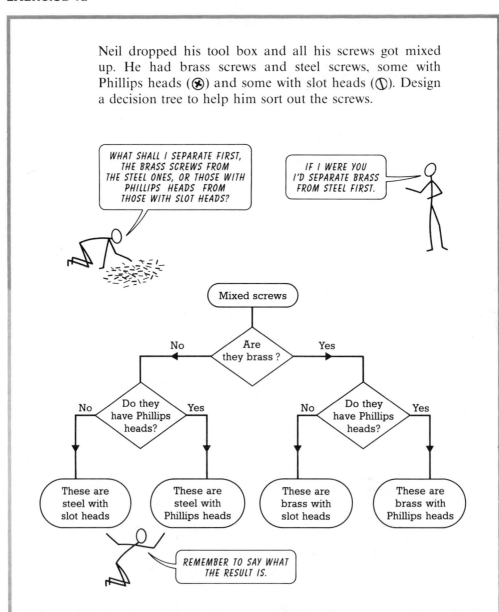

Neil dropped his tool box and all his screws got mixed up. He had brass screws and steel screws, some with Phillips heads (⊛) and some with slot heads (Ⓝ). Design a decision tree to help him sort out the screws.

1. Neil could have decided to start sorting out his screws by first separating the slot heads from the Phillips heads. Draw the decision tree showing how to sort the screws in this way.

2. Jasmine wants to organise her box of mixed buttons. There are large ones, small ones, some with two holes and some with four holes.
    a) This decision tree shows how Jasmine can do the sorting if she starts by separating large from small buttons.
       Copy and complete the decision tree.

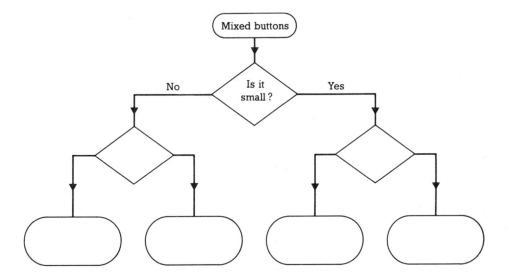

    b) Draw a decision tree which shows how Jasmine can do the sorting if she starts by separating two-hole buttons from four-hole ones.

3. Rachel has a lot of photographs. Some of them are of people and some are views. They are also of two different sizes, large and super. Draw a decision tree to show how Rachel can sort them out if she decides that the first step is to sort them by size.

4. In a cutlery drawer there is a mixture of stainless steel and silver-plated knives and forks. The cutlery can be sorted in two ways.
    a) Give the two different ways of starting.
    b) Draw a decision tree for each method.

Sometimes there is more sorting to do.

One afternoon Stewart wanted to find out how many red, green and silver cars passed his house. For each car that was one of these colours he noted the colour and also whether the car was a saloon or an estate. Show how he could sort out his list by drawing a decision tree.

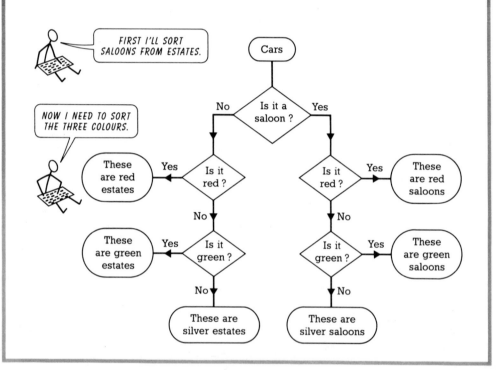

5. Sally has a drawer full of cassettes, some country and western, some pop and some classical. The tapes are also a mixture of 60-minute and 90-minute ones. Decide on a good way to sort them out and draw the decision tree.

6. A delivery of fish has just arrived at "Underwater World" and the different fish have to be sorted into the correct tanks. There are goldfish, orfe and rudd, and the 3–4 inch long fish must be separated from the ones that are 5–6 inches long.
    a) How many tanks are needed?
    b) Write down a suitable label for each tank, e.g. 3–4 inch rudd.
    c) Design a decision tree to plan the sorting.

A decision tree can "grow" if further sorting is needed. In the Worked Example on pages 3–4, for instance, Neil might also want to separate long screws from short ones.

If he did, a third question – "Are they long?" – would be asked at the end of each of the four "branches" in the decision tree. There would then be eight piles of sorted screws.

A second-hand book trader has to sort out a box of assorted books. He decides to separate hardbacks from paperbacks, novels from non-fiction and books in good condition from the poor quality ones. Draw a decision tree to show how the sorting might be done.

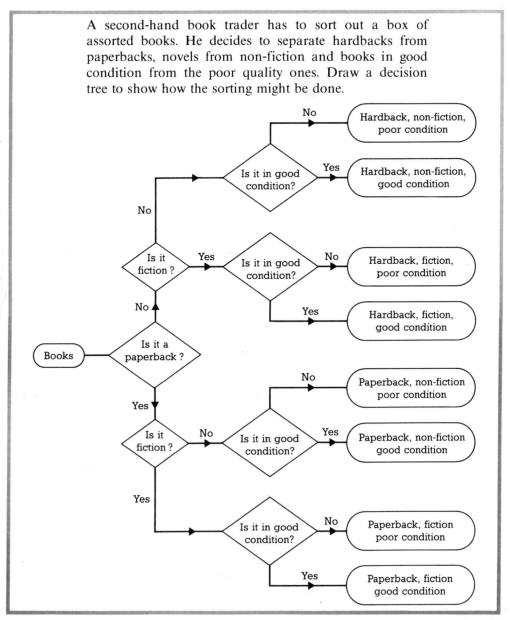

7. Mrs Brown is tidying her kitchen cupboard which contains both large and small sizes of tins and bottles, containing fruit and vegetables. She wants to separate all of these types. Design a decision tree to help with the sorting.

8. A carpet salesman wants to sort out his samples, separating Wilton from Axminster, plain from patterned and top quality from standard.

    a) Draw a suitable decision tree.
    b) How many separate piles of samples will he have?

9. All the first-year pupils in Rentworth School are being separated into groups. Their teacher is separating boys from girls, and those whose age is under 12 from those 12 and over. She also sorts out those wearing school uniform from those who are not.

    a) How many groups of pupils will there be after all the sorting is finished?
    b) Draw *two* decision trees which show how the sorting can be done if the teacher insists on first dividing girls from boys.
    c) Do we end up with the same groups in each tree?

2 PARALLEL LINES

PARALLEL LINES

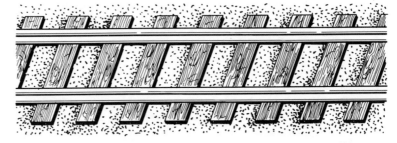

If two or more lines go in the same direction they are called parallel lines.

The rails in the drawing are parallel lines.

Two parallel lines are always the same distance apart.

EXERCISE 2a **1.** Write down five more everyday examples of parallel lines.

2. Draw two parallel lines (you can use two of the lines in your exercise book but make sure that they are at least 4 cm apart). Then draw a slant line crossing both lines, like the one shown below.

THESE ARROWS SHOW THAT THE LINES ARE PARALLEL.

MAKE THIS PART OF THE LINE AT LEAST 5 cm LONG.

Measure the angles marked *x* and *y*.
What do you notice?

3. Draw another pair of parallel lines, then draw a crossing line in a different direction from the one on page 7. Mark the angles *x* and *y* as before.

Measure the angles marked *x* and *y* and say what you notice.

Do all this again with several more pairs of parallel lines and different crossing lines. In some of your drawings, make sure that *x* and *y* are obtuse angles.

You will have found that *x* and *y* are about equal every time.

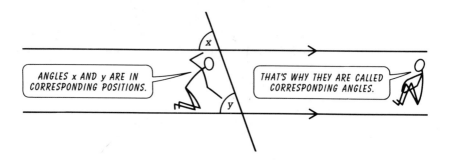

ANGLES x AND y ARE IN CORRESPONDING POSITIONS.

THAT'S WHY THEY ARE CALLED CORRESPONDING ANGLES.

CORRESPONDING ANGLES

We saw from Exercise 1a that

when a line crosses a set of parallel lines
the corresponding angles are equal.

It is quite easy to spot corresponding angles in a diagram if we look for an F shape (remember that the F may be slanting or turned over).

EXERCISE 2b In each question copy the diagram and draw the F shape in colour. Write down the angle corresponding to the shaded angle.

1.
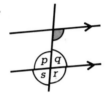

5.
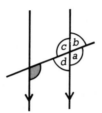

9.
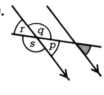

2.
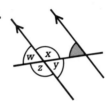

6.
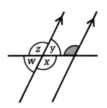

10.
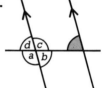

3.
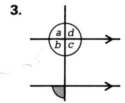

7.
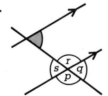

11.
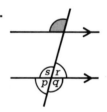

4.
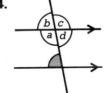

8.
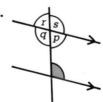

12.
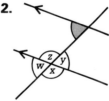

EXERCISE 2c In this exercise you also need to use the fact that angles on a straight line add up to 180°,

e.g.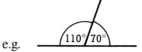

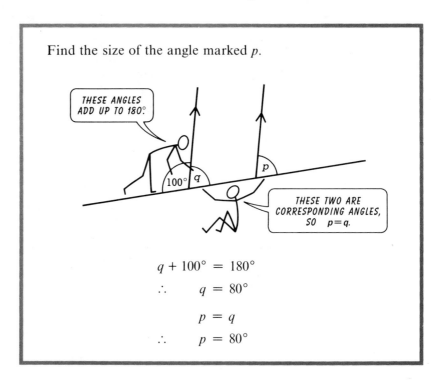

Find the size of the angle marked *p*.

THESE ANGLES ADD UP TO 180°.

THESE TWO ARE CORRESPONDING ANGLES, SO *p*=*q*.

$$q + 100° = 180°$$
$$\therefore \quad q = 80°$$
$$p = q$$
$$\therefore \quad p = 80°$$

In each question draw the F shape in colour then find the size of the angle marked *p*.

1.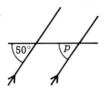

3.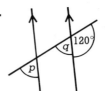

5.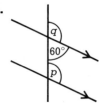

2.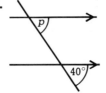

4.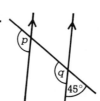

6.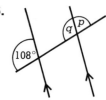

EXERCISE 2d In this exercise you can also use the fact that vertically opposite angles are equal.

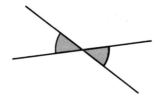

Find the size of the angle marked x.

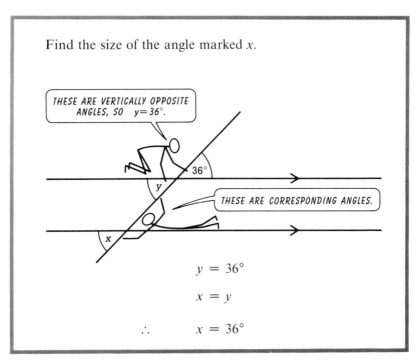

THESE ARE VERTICALLY OPPOSITE ANGLES, SO $y = 36°$.

36°

y

THESE ARE CORRESPONDING ANGLES.

x

$$y = 36°$$

$$x = y$$

$$\therefore \quad x = 36°$$

In Questions 1 to 6 find the size of each angle marked x.

1.

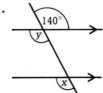

140°

y

x

3.

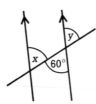

y

x 60°

5.

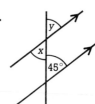

y

x

45°

2.

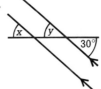

x y

30°

4.

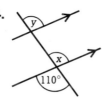

y

x

110°

6.

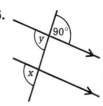

y 90°

x

DRawING PARALLEL LINES

Using 1 cm dot grid paper makes drawing parallel lines very simple.

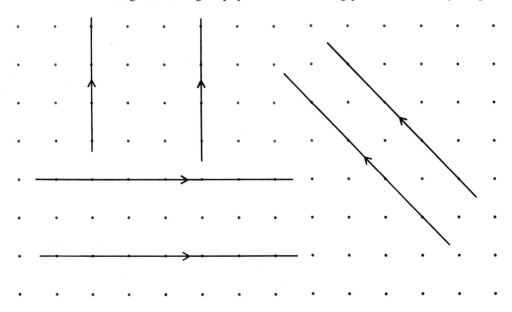

It is also easy to use the lines in your exercise book.

EXERCISE 2e Draw each pair of parallel lines on 1 cm dot grid paper.

   1. Two parallel lines, 4 cm apart, across the page.

   2. Two parallel lines, 5 cm apart, up the page.

   3. A pair of parallel lines, 3 cm apart, up the page.

   4. A pair of parallel lines, $4\frac{1}{2}$ cm apart, across the page.

ALTERNATE ANGLES ━━━━━━━━━━━━

EXERCISE 2f **1.** a) Draw two parallel lines that are about 3 cm apart, using dot grid paper or a pair of lines in your exercise book.

b) Draw a crossing line like the one shown below. Then mark the Z shape in a different colour.

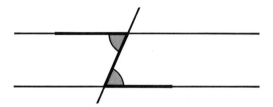

c) Measure the shaded angles. What do you notice?

2. Repeat Question 1 with another pair of parallel lines and a crossing line in a different direction.

> The shaded angles are called *alternate angles*.

> When a line crosses a pair of parallel lines the alternate angles are equal.

Looking for a Z shape helps in finding alternate angles. (Remember that the Z may not be level and it can be the wrong way round or very spread out.)

  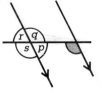

EXERCISE 2g In each question draw the Z shape in colour and write down the angle that is alternate to the shaded angle.

1.  **2.** **3.**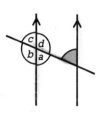

4.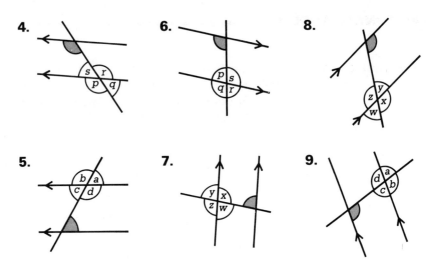

6.

8.

5.

7.

9.

EXERCISE 2h In this exercise you may need to use angles on a straight line and vertically opposite angles as well as corresponding angles and alternate angles.

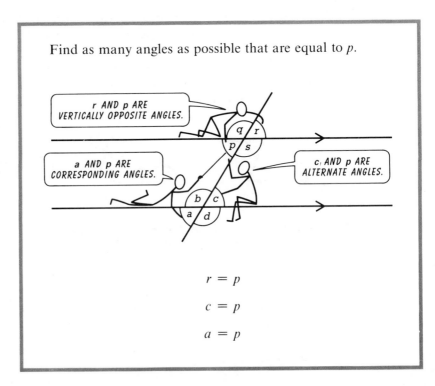

Find as many angles as possible that are equal to p.

r AND p ARE VERTICALLY OPPOSITE ANGLES.

a AND p ARE CORRESPONDING ANGLES.

c_i AND p ARE ALTERNATE ANGLES.

$$r = p$$

$$c = p$$

$$a = p$$

For each question copy the diagram and write down as many angles as you can find that are equal to p.

1.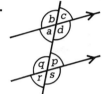

3.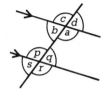

5.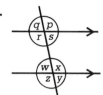

2.

4.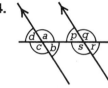

6.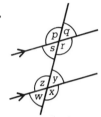

EXERCISE 2i

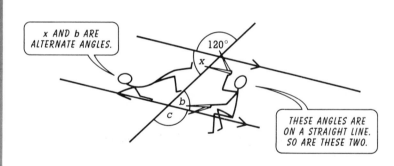

Find the sizes of the angles marked b and c.

x AND b ARE ALTERNATE ANGLES.

THESE ANGLES ARE ON A STRAIGHT LINE. SO ARE THESE TWO.

$$x + 120° = 180°$$

$$\therefore \qquad x = 60°$$

$$b = x$$

$$\therefore \qquad b = 60°$$

$$b + c = 180°$$

$$\therefore \qquad 60° + c = 180°$$

$$\therefore \qquad c = 120°$$

EXERCISE 2i   Find the size of each shaded angle.

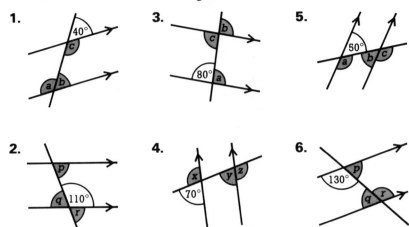

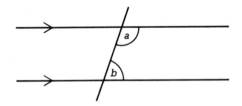

INTERIOR ANGLES

We are going to look at another pair of angles formed when a line crosses two parallel lines.

Angles *a* and *b* are called *interior angles*.

ANGLES a AND b ARE BOTH <u>INSIDE</u> THE PARALLEL LINES AND THEY ARE ON THE <u>SAME</u> SIDE OF THE CROSSING LINE.

A pair of interior angles can be spotted by looking for a U shape.

EXERCISE 2j　Copy each diagram roughly and shade a pair of interior angles.

1.

4.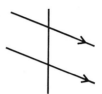

2.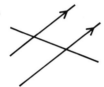

5.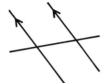

3.

6.

7. Use the lines of your exercise book to draw two parallel lines and a crossing line like the ones in this diagram.

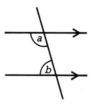

Measure *a* and *b* and add them together.

8. Repeat Question 7 with the crossing line in a different direction.

From your answers to Question 7 and 8 you will see that

interior angles add up to 180°

EXERCISE 2k

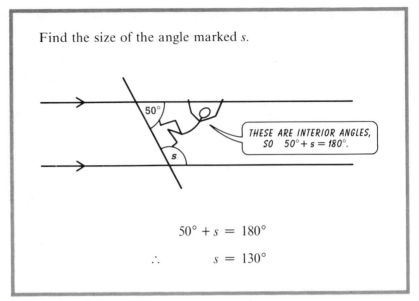

Find the size of the angle marked *s*.

50° THESE ARE INTERIOR ANGLES, SO 50° + s = 180°.

$$50° + s = 180°$$

$$\therefore \qquad s = 130°$$

Find the size of each marked angle.

1.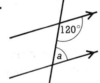

3.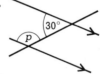

5.

2.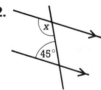

4.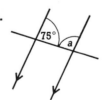

6.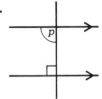

MIXED EXERCISE

EXERCISE 2l   The questions in this exercise may include any of the special angles from this chapter, i.e. vertically opposite angles, angles on a straight line, corresponding angles, alternate angles and interior angles. Remember that it can help to look for an F shape, a Z shape or a U shape.

In Questions 1 to 6 write down the angle or angles that are equal to the shaded angle.

1.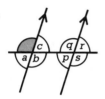

3.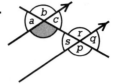

5.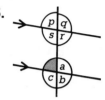

2.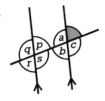

4.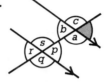

6.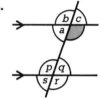

In Questions 7 to 12 find the size of the angle marked *x*.

7.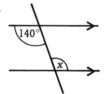

9.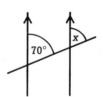

11.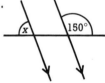

8.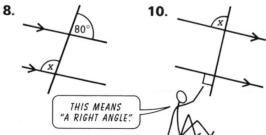

10.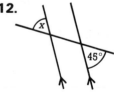

12.

3 WHOLE NUMBERS 1

PLACE VALUE

EXERCISE 3a

> In the number 627, find the value of
> a) the 6   b) the 2.
>
>
> a) The 6 has the value 6 hundreds, i.e. 600.
> b) The 2 has the value 2 tens, i.e. 20.

1. Underline the hundreds figure in 524. What is its value?

2. What is the value of the 5 in 745?

3. What is the value of the 9 in 497?

4. In 361, find the difference between the value of the 6 and the value of the 3.

CALCULATIONS

EXERCISE 3b Use this exercise to check that you can do basic arithmetic.

Find

1. $3 + 6 + 8$	**6.** 8×9	**11.** $24 - 6$
2. 3×6	**7.** 23×3	**12.** $24 \div 6$
3. $3 + 6 - 8$	**8.** $20 \div 4$	**13.** $24 + 6$
4. $8 - 3 + 6$	**9.** 20×4	**14.** 24×6
5. $3 \times 2 \times 4$	**10.** $23 + 45$	**15.** $48 + 29$

20

16.

| COFFEE 26 p | BUNS | ROLLS |
| TEA 23 p | 22 p each | 16 p each |

Work out the bills for the following people.

a) Gemma had two cups of coffee and a bun.

b) Alan drank a cup of tea and ate a roll and then, still being hungry, had a bun.

c) John paid for Georgy and himself. They had, between them, three coffees, two buns and a roll.

17. Some Smarties were shared amongst three people. Jane had 6, Aziz had twice as many as Jane and Lizzie had seven times as many as Aziz.

a) How many did Lizzie have?

b) How many Smarties were there altogether?

c) How many more did Lizzie have than Aziz?

EXERCISE 3c Use a calculator in this exercise. Check that your answers are sensible.

FOR INSTANCE, $60 \div 3$ WOULDN'T BE AS BIG AS 180.

Find

1. $345 + 23$ **3.** 45×14 **5.** $125 \div 25$

2. $124 - 89$ **4.** $120 \div 15$ **6.** $13 + 34 + 9$

Mrs Pollard is making 8 curtains.

7. Each curtain needs a 151 cm length of curtain tape. What is the smallest amount of tape she must get?

8. She allows a length of 186 cm of material for one curtain. This includes 19 cm for the top and the hem. How long will the curtain be when she has finished it?

Mrs Pollard is now deciding on the length of material to buy. She needs 6 lengths each of 186 cm and 2 each of 112 cm.

9. How many centimetres of material does she need?

10. She decides to buy 45 cm extra. How much does she now need?

MIXED OPERATIONS

Sometimes we are given several numbers and several operations, e.g. $2 \times 4 + 6$ or $9 - 2 \times 4$ and we need to know in what order to work them out.

Anything in brackets is worked out first.

For example,
$$(2 + 5) \times 3 = 7 \times 3$$
$$= 21$$

Multiplication and division come next, before addition and subtraction.

For example,
$$8 + 6 \times 2 = 8 + (6 \times 2)$$
$$= 8 + 12$$
$$= 20$$

Notice that $(8 + 6) \times 2$, which is 28, is not the same as $8 + 6 \times 2$.

EXERCISE 3d Do not use a calculator in this exercise.

Find a) $(2 + 4) \times 3$

b) $2 + 4 \times 3$

c) $2 - 4 \div 2$

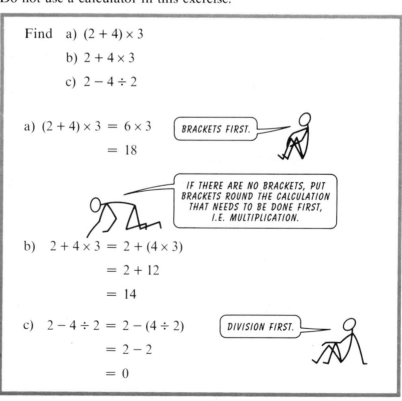

a) $(2 + 4) \times 3 = 6 \times 3$
$$= 18$$

BRACKETS FIRST.

IF THERE ARE NO BRACKETS, PUT BRACKETS ROUND THE CALCULATION THAT NEEDS TO BE DONE FIRST, I.E. MULTIPLICATION.

b) $2 + 4 \times 3 = 2 + (4 \times 3)$
$$= 2 + 12$$
$$= 14$$

c) $2 - 4 \div 2 = 2 - (4 \div 2)$
$$= 2 - 2$$
$$= 0$$

DIVISION FIRST.

Find

1. $(6 + 2) \times 4$ (Brackets first.)

2. $6 + 2 \times 4$ (Multiplication first.)

3. $6 \times (2 + 4)$ (Brackets first.)

4. $6 \div 2 + 4$ (Division first.)

5. $6 \times 2 + 4$ **9.** $9 \div 3 - 2$

6. $6 \times 2 - 4$ **10.** $12 - 4 \div 2$

7. $6 - 4 \div 2$ **11.** $(12 - 4) \div 2$

8. $(8 - 4) \times 3$ **12.** $12 \div 4 - 2$

13. $24 - 8 \div 2$ **17.** $(8 + 4) \times 3$

14. $(24 - 8) \div 2$ **18.** $8 + 4 \times 3$

15. $24 \div 8 - 2$ **19.** $(8 + 4) \div 3$

16. $24 \div (8 - 2)$ **20.** $8 \div 4 + 3$

MULTIPLICATION BY 10, 100, ETC.

Remember that if you multiply 4 by 100, then 4 becomes the number of hundreds, i.e. 400

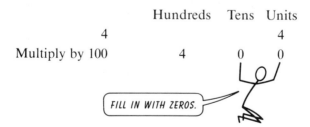

	Hundreds	Tens	Units
4			4
Multiply by 100	4	0	0

FILL IN WITH ZEROS.

	Hundreds	Tens	Units
30		3	0
Multiply by 10	3	0	0

So $30 \times 10 = 300$

Notice that the figures move to the left when multiplying by 10, 100 etc.

EXERCISE 3e

Find   a) 6×100 b) 70×10

a) $6 \times 100 = 600$

b) $70 \times 10 = 700$

Find

1. 3×10 **3.** 2×1000 **5.** 40×100

2. 5×100 **4.** 24×10 **6.** 16×100

7. 6×1000 **9.** 120×10 **11.** 90×10

8. 800×10 **10.** 24×100 **12.** 900×10

MULTIPLICATION BY MULTIPLES OF 10, 100

EXERCISE 3f

Find 40×200

$40 \times 200 = 40 \times 2 \times 100$

200 IS 2×100.
MULTIPLY BY THE 2 FIRST.

$= 80 \times 100$

$= 8000$

Find

1. 20×30 **3.** 12×30 **5.** 50×300

2. 200×20 **4.** 4000×2 **6.** 300×40

7. If each school coach will take 42 pupils, how many pupils will
100 coaches take?

8. A rectangle measures 42 cm by 10 cm.
What is its area?

DIVISION BY 10, 100 ETC. ▬▬▬▬▬▬▬▬▬▬▬▬

When multiplying by 10 or 100 or 1000 we move the figures to the *left*.

Division is the opposite of multiplication so if we want to divide by 10 we move the figures to the *right*.

	Hundreds	Tens	Units
700	7	0	0
Divide by 10		7	0

So $700 \div 10 = 70$

EXERCISE 3g

Find   a) $80 \div 10$ b) $940 \div 10$ c) $5000 \div 1000$

a) $80 \div 10 = 8$

b) $940 \div 10 = 94$

c) $5000 \div 1000 = 5$

Without using a calculator find

1. $400 \div 10$ **5.** $900 \div 10$

2. $6000 \div 100$ **6.** $2000 \div 1000$

3. $700 \div 100$ **7.** $120 \div 10$

4. $820 \div 10$ **8.** $6400 \div 10$

9.   A piece of string 640 cm long is to be cut into short pieces each 10 cm long.
How many 10 cm pieces will there be?

10.   Matchboxes can hold 100 matches each when full.
How many boxes will 3400 matches fill?

11.   How many tens does 600 represent?

12.   a) How many thousands does 4000 represent?
b) How many hundreds does it represent?
c) How many tens does it represent?

DIVISION BY MULTIPLES OF TEN

$60 \div 20$ is the same as 60 divided by 10 and then by 2.
$60 \div 10$ is 6, so now we divide 6 by 2 and get 3.

EXERCISE 3h

Find   a) $80 \div 40$ b) $900 \div 20$ c) $5000 \div 500$

a) $80 \div 40 = 2$

> DIVIDE BY 10;
> THIS GIVES 8.
> THEN DIVIDE BY 4.

b) $900 \div 20 = 90 \div 2$
$= 45$

> DIVIDE BY 10 FIRST,
> THEN BY 2.

c) $5000 \div 500 = 50 \div 5$
$= 10$

> DIVIDE BY 100 FIRST,
> THEN BY 5.

Without using a calculator find

1. $400 \div 40$ **5.** $900 \div 30$

2. $6000 \div 200$ **6.** $2000 \div 40$

3. $700 \div 100$ **7.** $120 \div 30$

4. $8000 \div 20$ **8.** $60\,000 \div 3000$

9. A school orders 800 exercise books. The books come in packs of 40.
How many packs are needed?

10. For the school play, 300 chairs are set out in rows of 20.
How many rows are there?

Find

11. 40×20 **14.** $600 \div 30$

12. $40 \div 20$ **15.** 8000×40

13. 600×30 **16.** $8000 \div 40$

SIZES OF NUMBERS

To save writing "is greater than" we can use the symbol >
and for "is less than" we use the symbol <

EXERCISE 3i   **1.**   Put in size order with the smallest first: 27, 702 and 207.

2.   Which is the greater, 67 or 76?

3.   Copy and complete the statement "13 is _____ than 9".

Write the following statements in figures and symbols.

a) "Seventy is greater than seven"

b) "Eleven is less than twenty"

a) 70 > 7

> MEANS "IS GREATER THAN".
> NOTICE THAT 70 IS AT
> THE WIDER END OF >.

b) 11 < 20

< MEANS "IS LESS THAN".

---

4.   Write in figures and symbols
   a) seven is less than eight
   b) nine is greater than two.

5.   Write in words
   a) 6 > 2   b) 8 < 12

6.   Copy and complete, with either < or >, each of the following
   statements.
   a) 10   3   b) 42   45   c) 51   15

ROUNDING

We often need to round a complicated number to a simpler one.

For instance, "six thousand, nine hundred and twenty four people attended the match" is difficult to grasp when you hear it. "About seven thousand people attended" gives a clearer picture.

EXERCISE 3j   1.

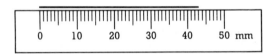

a) Give the length of the line in millimetres.
b) Give the length of the line to the nearest 10 mm.

2.

a) Give the temperature in degrees Celsius.
b) Give the temperature to the nearest ten degrees.

3. _____

Measure the length of the line to the nearest centimetre.

4. According to the catalogue, the senior school library has 5832 books. How many books are there, to the nearest thousand ?

5.

Collecting money for charity using a penny snake, 2856 pennies were laid out in the courtyard.

What simple round number could the organiser use to describe the number of pennies?

6.

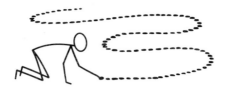

Copy and complete the following statement:

"About _____ thousand attended the match".

7. A seed packet contained 197 seeds. On the packet is printed

"This packet contains about _____ hundred seeds".

What is the missing word?

MORE ROUNDING

If we are asked to round 246 to the nearest hundred we can see that it is nearest to 200.

The hundreds figure is 2. Put in a dotted line after the 2, so that we have 2⦙4 6. Look at the next figure, 4. It is less than 5 and this helps us to decide that 246 is nearer to 200 than to 300.

Now suppose we are asked to give 827 to the nearest ten. The tens figure is 2 so put the dotted line after the 2.

We now have 8 2⦙7. The next figure, 7, is greater than 5 so 827 is nearer to 830 than to 820.

EXERCISE 3k

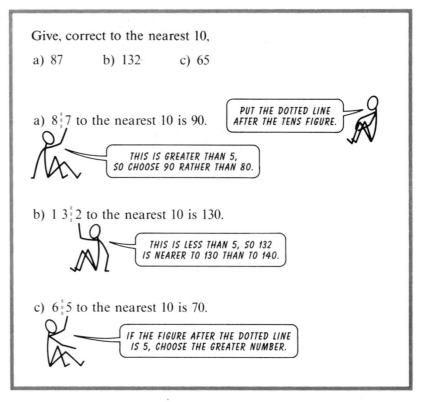

Give, correct to the nearest 10,

a) 87   b) 132   c) 65

a) 8ᐧ7 to the nearest 10 is 90.

PUT THE DOTTED LINE AFTER THE TENS FIGURE.

THIS IS GREATER THAN 5, SO CHOOSE 90 RATHER THAN 80.

b) 1 3ᐧ2 to the nearest 10 is 130.

THIS IS LESS THAN 5, SO 132 IS NEARER TO 130 THAN TO 140.

c) 6ᐧ5 to the nearest 10 is 70.

IF THE FIGURE AFTER THE DOTTED LINE IS 5, CHOOSE THE GREATER NUMBER.

Use dotted lines to help you to get the answers to all the questions in this exercise.

Give each number correct to the nearest ten.

1. 47	**3.** 38	**5.** 647	**7.** 125
2. 72	**4.** 512	**6.** 75	**8.** 384

9. 92	**11.** 13	**13.** 241	**15.** 119
10. 99	**12.** 27	**14.** 386	**16.** 121

17. a) Find 32×11
    b) Give your answer to the nearest ten.

18. a) Find, in pence, the sum of 81 p and 96 p.
    b) Give your answer to the nearest ten pence.

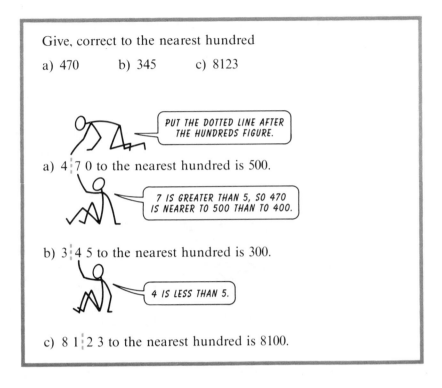

Give, correct to the nearest hundred

a) 470   b) 345   c) 8123

PUT THE DOTTED LINE AFTER THE HUNDREDS FIGURE.

a) 4 ┊ 7 0 to the nearest hundred is 500.

7 IS GREATER THAN 5, SO 470 IS NEARER TO 500 THAN TO 400.

b) 3 ┊ 4 5 to the nearest hundred is 300.

4 IS LESS THAN 5.

c) 8 1 ┊ 2 3 to the nearest hundred is 8100.

In Questions 19 to 22, give each number correct to the nearest hundred.

19. 674

20. 7840

21. 2230

22. 9256

23.    Give this number to the nearest hundred.

24. John measured the length of the kitchen and found that it was 482 cm.

a) Give the length to the nearest 100 cm.

b) Give the length to the nearest 10 cm.

25. a) Use your calculator to find 42×26.

b) Give your answer to the nearest hundred.

26. Angela bought 9 pairs of tights at 93 p each.

    a) What is the total bill in pence?

    b) What is the bill to the nearest ten pence?

27. The box contains 228 tacks.

Approximate contents: . . . tacks

    a) The missing number is not 228. What do *you* think is the missing number?

    b) Is your answer given to the nearest 10 or nearest 100 tacks?

28.

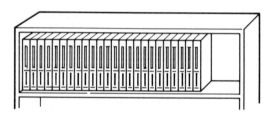

Each mathematics textbook is 16 mm wide. There are 24 of these textbooks on the shelf.

    a) In millimetres, how wide a space do they take up?

    b) What is the width of the space to the nearest 10 mm?

    c) Give the width of the space to the nearest centimetre.

ROUGH ESTIMATES

£8.40

I'VE ONLY BOUGHT 5 PAIRS OF TIGHTS AT 95 PENCE EACH. CAN £8.40 BE RIGHT?

Being able to give large numbers to the nearest ten or hundred enables us to get a rough answer to a multiplication. e.g. 5×95 is approximately equal to 5×100.

(So we know that Jane's bill for the tights should be about 500 p and she is being charged too much.)

EXERCISE 3I **1.** Andy is buying 4 pairs of socks at 72 p each. Give a rough estimate of the total cost.

WORK WITH 70p
INSTEAD OF 72p.

2. Ballpoint pens cost 19 p each. Find a rough estimate of the total cost of 9 pens.

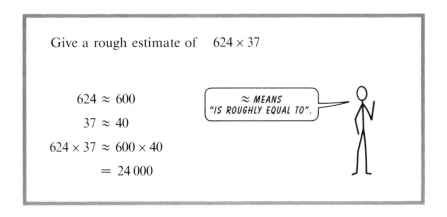

Give a rough estimate of 624×37

$624 \approx 600$

$37 \approx 40$

$624 \times 37 \approx 600 \times 40$

$= 24\,000$

≈ MEANS
"IS ROUGHLY EQUAL TO".

Give a rough estimate of the answer to each of the following calculations.

3. 4×69 **4.** 32×19 **5.** 870×3

6. In Mark's postcard collection there are 62 pages, each with 8 cards.
Roughly how many cards are there altogether?

7. For a picnic, roughly how many sandwiches should be made for 72 children if each child eats about 5 sandwiches?

8. In the school canteen, about 680 yoghurts are eaten each week. Roughly how many yoghurts are eaten in 11 weeks?

9. Find a rough value for 39×240.
Which of the following numbers is most likely to be the exact answer?

a) 2160   b) 9360   c) 34 760   d) 460

CHECKING ANSWERS ━━━━━━━━━━━━━━━━━━━━━━

EXERCISE 3m

Find a rough estimate for the answer to 342×58 and then use your calculator to find the exact answer.

$$342 \approx 300$$
$$58 \approx 60$$
$$342 \times 58 \approx 300 \times 60$$
$$= 18\,000$$
$$342 \times 58 = 19\,836 \quad \text{(using a calculator)}$$

19 836 AGREES QUITE WELL WITH THE ESTIMATE, SO IT IS LIKELY TO BE CORRECT.

In each question from 1 to 6,

a) find a rough estimate of the answer,

b) work out the answer using a calculator.

Do your answers agree fairly well?

1. 47×32 **4.** 5×380

2. 11×99 **5.** 23×71

3. 102×41 **6.** 38×3

7. Oliver wanted a carpet in the sitting room. He needed 27 square metres of carpet, costing £17 a square metre. First he worked out roughly how much it would cost, then he found the exact amount.
Write down his two answers.

8. Sarah worked out a rough estimate for 38×112 and then used her calculator to find the exact answer.
Her exact answer was 2256. She decided she must have pressed the wrong buttons.
What made her decide this?
What is the correct answer?

9. Some pupils were asked to find the value of 48×232

a) Susan used her calculator and got 1116. Without using your calculator decide whether her answer is likely to be correct or not. Give your reason.

b) Bena worked it out to be 11 116 and Malcolm got 19 136. Which one of the two is nearer to the correct answer? (Do not use your calculator to help you to decide this.)

c) Now use your calculator to find the correct answer. Were any of the three pupils correct?

ROUNDING A NUMBER TO THE NEAREST WHOLE NUMBER

If we divide 234 by 11 using a calculator, the display shows $21 \cdot 2727 \ldots$

Sometimes we need the answer to the nearest whole number. In this case we have to choose between 21 and 22. As before we look at the next figure after the units. It is less than 5 so we choose the smaller number, 21.

EXERCISE 3n Use a calculator in this exercise.

Find $456 \div 14$ and give the answer to the nearest whole number.

32·5714... APPEARS ON THE DISPLAY. CHOOSE BETWEEN 32 AND 33. THE FIGURE AFTER THE UNITS FIGURE IS 5, SO WE CHOOSE THE GREATER.

$456 \div 14 = 33$, to the nearest whole number.

In Questions 1 to 4, give the answers to the nearest whole number.

1. $791 \div 46$ **3.** $310 \div 34$

2. $364 \div 23$ **4.** $765 \div 31$

5. ⊨━━━•━━━━•━━━━•━━━━•━━━━•━━━━•━━━▶

Seven equal matchsticks laid end to end measure 22 cm. To the nearest centimetre, what is the length of one matchstick?

6. £170 is shared equally between 3 sisters.
To the nearest £, how much will they each get?

7. A piece of string 500 cm long is cut into 19 pieces.
What is the length of each piece to the nearest cm?

8. Gerry walked 3060 cm in 47 equal paces.
To the nearest centimetre, what is the length of one pace?

9. Angela covers 360 m by swimming 27 lengths of the hotel pool.
What, to the nearest metre, is the length of the pool?

10. When Sally travels 2000 cm, her bicycle wheel rotates 13 times.
To the nearest centimetre, how far does she travel if the wheel rotates once?

MIXED EXERCISES ━━━━━━━━━━━━━━━━━━━━━━━━━━━━━━

EXERCISE 3p **1.** Find   a) $7 - 3 \times 2$ b) $(7 - 3) \times 2$

2. Give 472 to the nearest ten.

3. Find $1024 \div 32$

4. Find 30×30 without using a calculator.

5. Fill in the spaces with $<$ or $>$
a) 11   17   b) 23   19

EXERCISE 3q **1.** Find $9 + 4 \times 2$

2. Find 14×82 and give the answer to the nearest 100.

3. Find 3100 ÷ 10 without using a calculator.

4. Find 431 + 39

5. One of the following statements is false.
Find it and write a correct version.
a) 14 > 13   b) 7 > 10

EXERCISE 3r **1.** Find a) 22 − 14 ÷ 2 b) (10 − 6) ÷ 2

2. Without using a calculator, find 570 ÷ 10

3. Give 9876 a) to the nearest ten
b) to the nearest hundred.

4. Copy these numbers and put < or > in the space.
a) 21   12   b) 69   71

5. Use a calculator to find 271 ÷ 13 to the nearest whole number.

4 WHOLE NUMBERS 2

DIVISION WITH REMAINDERS

If we multiply whole numbers together the answer is a whole number and the same is true of addition and subtraction.

However, if we divide one whole number by another we may not always get a whole number answer. For instance, $9 \div 2$ gives 4 with a remainder of 1 unit.

EXERCISE 4a Make sure your answers are of a sensible size.

> Small cakes are packed in boxes of eight. How many boxes will 68 cakes fill and how many cakes will be left over?
>
> $68 \div 8 = 8$, rem 4 $8 \times 8 = 64$ AND $68 - 64 = 4$
>
> The cakes will fill 8 boxes with 4 cakes over.

1.

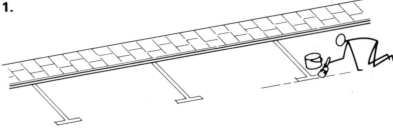

Car-parking spaces are marked off along the side of a road 37 m long. Each car space is 5 m long.

How many car spaces can be marked and how much space is left at the end of the road?

2. Electric light bulbs are packed 9 to the box.
How many boxes will 80 bulbs fill and how many bulbs will be left over?

3. Divide 39 by 7 and give the remainder.

What is the remainder when 67 is divided by 3?

$$\begin{array}{r} 22 \\ 3\,\overline{)\,67} \end{array} \quad \text{rem 1}$$

The remainder is 1.

3 INTO 6 FIRST,
THEN 3 INTO 7.

Find the remainder in each of the following calculations.

4. 69 ÷ 6   **6.** 49 ÷ 2   **8.** 142 ÷ 7

5. 98 ÷ 3   **7.** 81 ÷ 8   **9.** 108 ÷ 5

10. In a block of flats each flat-owner gives £3 a week to a fund for cleaning and gardening. The total collected is £63.
How many flat-owners are there?

11. In a cutlery box, each slot takes 6 forks.
How many slots will be needed for 128 forks?
How many forks will there be in the last, partly filled, slot?

12. Twenty-pence pieces are counted by putting them in piles of 5 coins.
a) What is the value of each pile?
b) If there are 58 coins, how many complete piles are there?
c) How many coins are there in the last, incomplete, pile?
d) What is the total value of the 58 coins?

DIVISION USING REMAINDERS

EXERCISE 4b Make sure that each of the answers is a sensible size.

Find how many times 6 goes into 525 and give the remainder.

So 525 ÷ 6 = 87 with remainder 3.

1. Find how many times 4 goes into 435 and give the remainder.

2. Divide 456 by 5, giving a whole number answer and the remainder.

In Questions 3 to 8, give whole number answers and the remainders.

3. 734 ÷ 6	**5.** 111 ÷ 2	**7.** 288 ÷ 9
4. 135 ÷ 7	**6.** 98 ÷ 5	**8.** 169 ÷ 3

9.

Mrs. Brown is filling small baskets with Easter eggs. She has 140 eggs and is putting 6 eggs in each basket.

How many baskets will she be able to fill and will there be any eggs left over?

10. In a competition, 5 children won a prize of £96 and shared out as much of it as they could so that they had an equal number of pounds each. They gave the money that was over to a charity.

How much did each of them have and how much went to the charity?

11. Mr. Martin had 187 screws for the pupils in his woodwork class. He gave them 8 each and had less than 8 left over.

How many pupils were there in his class and how many screws had he left?

12. A group of 167 people were asked to get into teams of 9.

How many teams of 9 were there and how many people were left to form a smaller team?

13. Eight shelves each hold the same number of books. Miss Jones has 342 books which need to be put on to the shelves but she finds that there is not quite room for all of them. How many are there on each shelf and how many are there left over?

14. An egg box holds 6 eggs. How many egg boxes are needed to hold 253 eggs? How many empty spaces will there be in the last box?

DIVISION BY A NUMBER BIGGER THAN 10

If the number we are dividing is bigger than 10, we need to allow more space for writing the remainders.

We can write the remainders below the given numbers, instead of above.

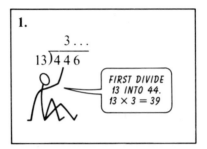

1. FIRST DIVIDE 13 INTO 44. 13 × 3 = 39

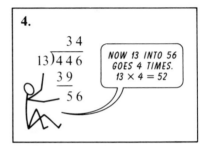

4. NOW 13 INTO 56 GOES 4 TIMES. 13 × 4 = 52

2. TAKE 39 FROM 44 AND PUT THE REMAINDER 5 UNDERNEATH.

5. TAKE 52 FROM 56. THE LAST REMAINDER IS 4.

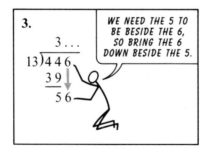

3. WE NEED THE 5 TO BE BESIDE THE 6, SO BRING THE 6 DOWN BESIDE THE 5.

6. SO 446 ÷ 13 = 34, REMAINDER 4.

NOTICE THAT THIS METHOD IS THE SAME AS THE PREVIOUS ONE BUT THE FIGURES ARE IN DIFFERENT PLACES.

EXERCISE 4c Do not use a calculator in this exercise.

Find 588 ÷ 12

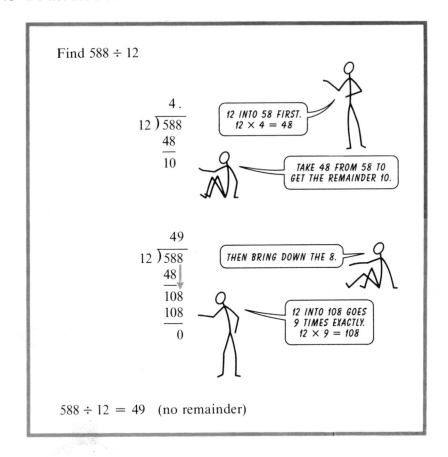

588 ÷ 12 = 49   (no remainder)

In Questions 1 to 6, there are no final remainders.

Find

1. 121 ÷ 11   **3.** 156 ÷ 12   **5.** 315 ÷ 15

2. 294 ÷ 14   **4.** 273 ÷ 21   **6.** 484 ÷ 22

In Questions 7 to 12, there *are* final remainders.

Find

7. 278 ÷ 13   **9.** 313 ÷ 23   **11.** 367 ÷ 32

8. 712 ÷ 11   **10.** 481 ÷ 22   **12.** 562 ÷ 12

13. A piece of dowel 255 centimetres long is cut into 15 pieces all of the same length.
How long is each piece?

14. £2 is shared out between 15 people.
How much do they each get and how many pence are there over?

15. Thirteen people are each giving an equal number of £s to charity. The target is £217.
How much should each give so that the target is reached?

MULTIPLICATION BY NUMBERS BIGGER THAN 10

If we are multiplying 23 by 12, say, we need to multiply 23 by 2 and by 10 because $12 = 10 + 2$.

We write the results of the two multiplications and add them together.

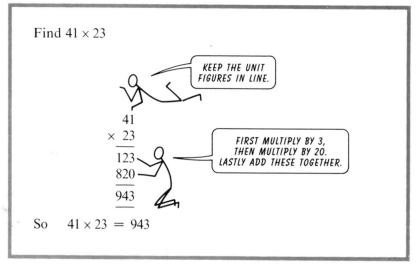

EXERCISE 4d

Do not use a calculator in this exercise.

Find

1. 32×21 **3.** 28×14 **5.** 34×34

2. 43×16 **4.** 56×11 **6.** 64×16

7. A milk crate holds 24 bottles.
How many bottles are there in 21 full crates?

8. A computer printer prints 66 lines per page.
How many lines are there on 34 pages?

9. In the school kitchen, there are 36 piles of plates, each containing 15 plates.
How many plates are there altogether?

MIXED MULTIPLICATION AND DIVISION

EXERCISE 4e   **1.**   a) Without using a calculator, find 45×32
          b) Check your answer to (a) by using your calculator.

      2.   a) Without using a calculator, find $256 \div 16$
          b) Check your answer to (a) by using your calculator.

Do not use your calculator to answer the following questions.

CHICKEN	75 p
TUNA	72 p
SALAD	64 p

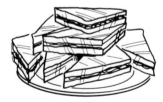

3. Jeremy is buying sandwiches for himself and his workmates.
He buys 12 chicken sandwiches and 11 salad sandwiches.
How much does he have to pay?

4. The next day, Jeremy bought 23 sandwiches, all at the same price. The bill was £16.56
What was the price of each sandwich?

WORK IN PENCE.

5.   Jeremy set off the next day with £16.
How many pence is this?
He bought as many salad sandwiches as he could.
How many did he buy and how much money was left over?

EXERCISE 4f **1.** a) Without using a calculator, find   63 × 24
b) Check your answer by using a calculator.

2. a) Without using a calculator, find   648 ÷ 24
b) Check your answer by using a calculator.

3. a) Multiply 62 by 15
b) Take the answer to part (a) and divide it by 31.

4. A running track is 132 m round.
a) John runs 13 circuits of the track.
     How far does he run?
b) Andreas runs 660 m; how many circuits of the track is this?

5. A class of 19 pupils is to carry out a project. The class teacher
distributes a pack of 350 sheets of paper so that each pupil gets
the same number of sheets.
a) How many pages does each pupil get?
b) How many sheets are left over?

5 FRACTIONS

THE MEANING OF FRACTIONS

EXERCISE 5a

Write down the fraction of the shape that is shaded.

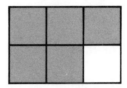

The fraction shaded is $\frac{5}{6}$

For each of the following sketches, write down the fraction of the shape that is shaded.

1.

4.

2.

5.

3.

6.

Write down the fraction that is

a) shaded,   b) not shaded.

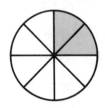

REMEMBER THAT FRACTIONS CAN BE SIMPLIFIED BY DIVIDING THE TOP AND THE BOTTOM BY THE SAME NUMBER.

a) The fraction shaded is $\frac{2}{8} = \frac{1}{4}$

b) The fraction not shaded is $\frac{6}{8} = \frac{3}{4}$

$\left(\text{Note that } \frac{1}{4} + \frac{3}{4} = \frac{4}{4} = 1\right)$

For each of the following sketches write down, in its simplest form, the fraction of the area that is

a) shaded,   b) not shaded.

7.

8.

9.

10.

11.

12.

Copy each shape and shade the fraction given in brackets. You can do this in more than one way.

13.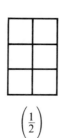
$\left(\frac{1}{2}\right)$

14.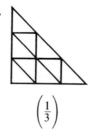
$\left(\frac{1}{3}\right)$

15.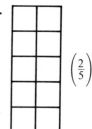
$\left(\frac{2}{5}\right)$

16.
$\left(\frac{5}{8}\right)$

17.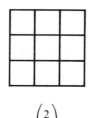
$\left(\frac{2}{3}\right)$

18.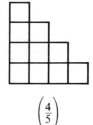
$\left(\frac{4}{5}\right)$

FRACTIONS OF A QUANTITY

Frequently in everyday life we need to find a fraction of a quantity. Maybe we need half a jug of milk, or three-quarters of a length of wood or two-thirds of a tin of raspberries.

EXERCISE 5b   **1.**   Draw a sketch of this jug four times.

Draw a line to show roughly the position of the surface when it is

a) half full
b) three-quarters full
c) two-thirds full
d) one-quarter full.

2. Repeat Question 1 for other jugs with different shapes, for example

a)   b)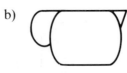

Find $\frac{1}{5}$ of 40

$\frac{1}{5}$ of 40 $= 40 \div 5$

$= 8$

I NEED TO DIVIDE 40 INTO 5 EQUAL PARTS. SO I MUST DIVIDE 40 BY 5.

3. Find

a) $\frac{1}{2}$ of 10   c) $\frac{1}{5}$ of 25   e) $\frac{1}{7}$ of 28   g) $\frac{1}{3}$ of 48

b) $\frac{1}{3}$ of 24   d) $\frac{1}{4}$ of 12   f) $\frac{1}{2}$ of 62   h) $\frac{1}{10}$ of 60

Find $\frac{3}{4}$ of 36

$\frac{1}{4}$ of 36 $= 9$

$\therefore$ $\frac{3}{4}$ of 36 $= 3 \times 9$

$= 27$

TO FIND $\frac{3}{4}$ OF 36, FIRST FIND $\frac{1}{4}$ OF 36, THEN MULTIPLY THE ANSWER BY 3.

4. Find

a) $\frac{3}{4}$ of 24   c) $\frac{3}{5}$ of 35   e) $\frac{3}{7}$ of 21   g) $\frac{3}{10}$ of 70

b) $\frac{2}{3}$ of 24   d) $\frac{2}{5}$ of 40   f) $\frac{5}{6}$ of 36   h) $\frac{4}{9}$ of 36

5. Use a calculator if necessary to find

a) $\frac{1}{7}$ of 105   d) $\frac{3}{4}$ of 68   g) $\frac{2}{3}$ of 117

b) $\frac{1}{12}$ of 168   e) $\frac{3}{5}$ of 435   h) $\frac{5}{7}$ of 105

c) $\frac{1}{5}$ of 435   f) $\frac{7}{10}$ of 660   i) $\frac{5}{9}$ of 126

6.

David gives $\frac{1}{3}$ of the biscuits in this packet to Sue and $\frac{1}{2}$ of them to Lorna.

a) How many biscuits does Sue get?
b) How many biscuits does Lorna get?
c) How many biscuits are left for David?

7.

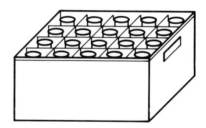

The milkman removes this crate of milk from his float. He delivers $\frac{1}{4}$ of the bottles to the Smiths and $\frac{2}{5}$ of them to the Baghdadis.

How many bottles of milk

a) do the Smiths get
b) do the Baghdadis get
c) are left in the crate?

8. Find

a) $\frac{3}{5}$ of 30 metres   d) $\frac{3}{7}$ of 21 miles   g) $\frac{3}{5}$ of 25 p

b) $\frac{3}{4}$ of £20   e) $\frac{5}{8}$ of 32 km   h) $\frac{3}{8}$ of 40 miles

c) $\frac{1}{2}$ of 120 litres   f) $\frac{2}{7}$ of 1 week   i) $\frac{5}{8}$ of 16 gallons

Find $\frac{2}{5}$ of £1

$$£1 = 100 \text{ pence}$$
$$\frac{1}{5} \text{ of } £1 = \frac{1}{5} \text{ of } 100 \text{ p}$$
$$= 20 \text{ p}$$
$$\frac{2}{5} \text{ of } £1 = 2 \times 20 \text{ p}$$
$$= 40 \text{ p}$$

9. In this question give your answer in the unit in brackets.

a) $\frac{3}{4}$ of £2 (pence)

f) $\frac{5}{12}$ of a year (months)

b) $\frac{4}{5}$ of 3 metres (cm)

g) $\frac{7}{10}$ of a metre (cm)

c) $\frac{3}{5}$ of £1 (pence)

h) $\frac{3}{8}$ of 4 cm (mm)

d) $\frac{2}{3}$ of 1 hour (minutes)

i) $\frac{5}{7}$ of 1 week (days)

e) $\frac{2}{5}$ of half an hour (minutes)   j) $\frac{5}{8}$ of 1 m (cm)

10. You may need a calculator for this question.
Find

a) $\frac{2}{5}$ of £125

f) $\frac{3}{8}$ of 104 mm

b) $\frac{5}{8}$ of 600 litres

g) $\frac{5}{9}$ of 675 dollars

c) $\frac{3}{4}$ of 224 km

h) $\frac{2}{7}$ of 392 francs

d) $\frac{7}{8}$ of 112 miles

i) $\frac{5}{12}$ of 324 days

e) $\frac{4}{7}$ of 161 cm

j) $\frac{4}{9}$ of 189 hours

The drawing shows the number of biscuits John has left after he has eaten $\frac{2}{3}$ of the packet.

How many biscuits were in the unopened packet?

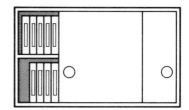

HE HAS EATEN $\frac{2}{3}$ OF THE PACKET. THEREFORE $\frac{1}{3}$ OF THE PACKET REMAINS.

$\frac{1}{3}$ of the packet is 6 biscuits.

∴ the number of biscuits in the packet is 3×6
i.e. 18 biscuits

---

11. Janet keeps her videos in a cupboard. She draws back the sliding door and can see $\frac{1}{3}$ of the videos on the top shelf and $\frac{1}{5}$ of the videos on the bottom shelf.

How many videos are there

a) on the top shelf   b) on the bottom shelf?

12. Jenny opens her kitchen cupboard to check its contents. She can see only the containers on the fronts of the shelves.

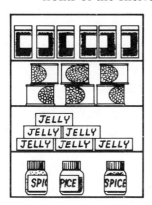

a) She can see $\frac{2}{3}$ of her jars of jam.
How many does she have altogether?

b) She can see $\frac{3}{4}$ of her tins of beans.
How many does she have altogether?

c) She can see $\frac{2}{5}$ of her packets of jelly.
How many does she have altogether?

d) She can see $\frac{3}{5}$ of her jars of spice.
How many does she have altogether?

6 SYMMETRY AND CONGRUENCE

LINE SYMMETRY

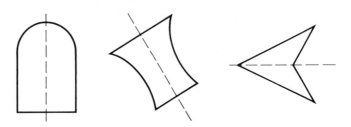

These shapes are *symmetrical*. They have line symmetry.

The dotted line is the line of symmetry, because if the shape is folded along the dotted line the two halves of the drawing fit exactly over each other.

EXERCISE 6a For each diagram, say whether or not the dotted line is a line of symmetry. Use a mirror if it helps.

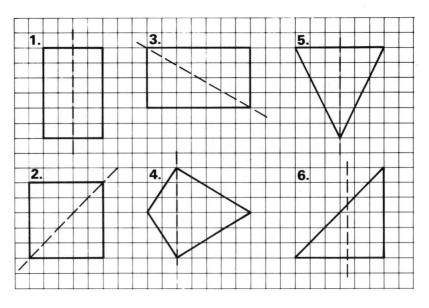

Copy these diagrams onto squared paper and then draw the line of symmetry. Use a dotted line or a coloured line.

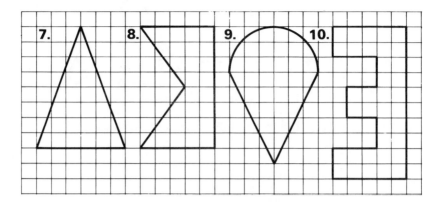

Copy the following drawings onto squared paper and complete them so that the dotted line is a line of symmetry.

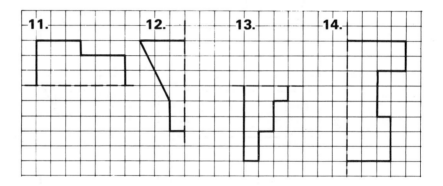

Some shapes have more than one line of symmetry.

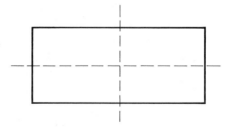

This rectangle has two lines of symmetry. These are shown by the dotted lines.

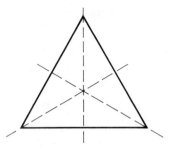

This triangle has three lines of symmetry.

EXERCISE 6b Copy these shapes and mark the lines of symmetry. Some of the shapes have more than one line of symmetry.

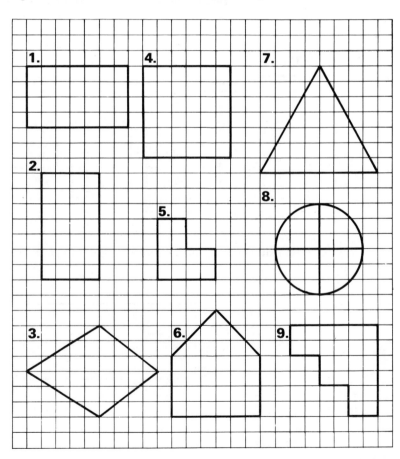

EXERCISE 6c Copy the following drawings onto squared paper and complete them so that the dotted lines are lines of symmetry.

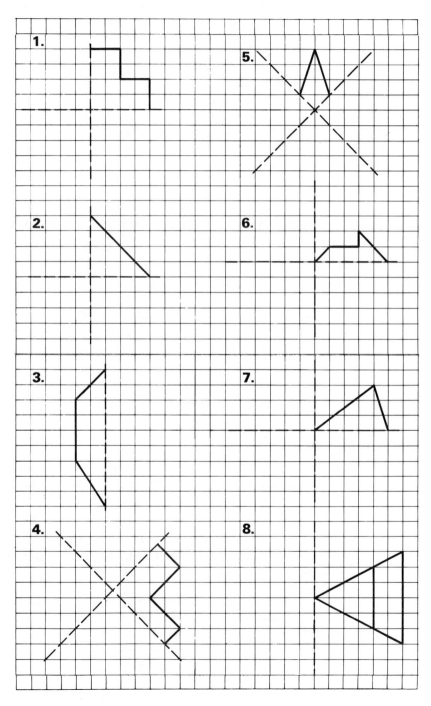

ROTATIONAL SYMMETRY

Have you seen this shape on the back of certain German cars?

The shape can be turned about its centre and still looks the same.

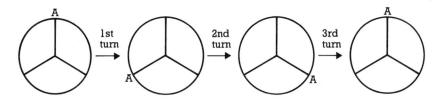

When the original shape is turned through one-third of a complete turn about its centre it still looks the same. If we follow one point A on the shape we can see that it requires three such turns before A is back at its starting point.

This shape has *rotational symmetry of order 3*.

EXERCISE 6d Give the order of rotational symmetry of each shape.

You can find this by tracing each shape and marking one point on the traced shape. Then turn the tracing paper about the centre point (use a compass point or pencil point on the centre) until the traced shape fits exactly over the original shape again.

The number of times that you can make it turn and fit, before getting the marked point back to its starting position, gives the order of rotational symmetry.

1.   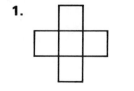   **2.**   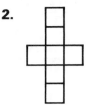   **3.**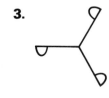

4. 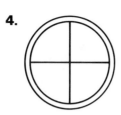 **7.** 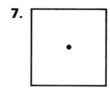 **10.**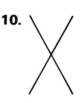

5. 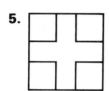 **8.** 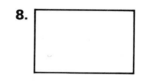 **11.**

6. 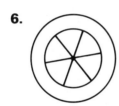 **9.** 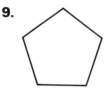 **12.**

13. Here are twelve road signs from the Highway Code. For each one say whether it has:

one line of symmetry; two lines of symmetry; more than two lines of symmetry; rotational symmetry; or no symmetry.

Remember that some may have both line symmetry and rotational symmetry.

Use tracing paper if it helps.

a) 　　b) 　　c)

ROTATING SHAPES

The position of the centre of rotation is important; it is usually marked with a cross. In each of the following diagrams, the shaded area is rotated through half a turn about the cross.

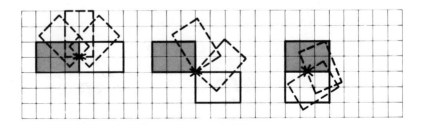

In each case the combined figure has rotational symmetry of order 2.

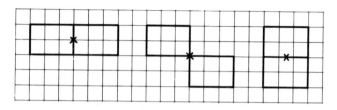

EXERCISE 6e In Questions 1 to 4, each shape is rotated through half a turn about the point marked with a cross, to give a figure with rotational symmetry.

Copy the shapes onto squared paper and use tracing paper to show the complete figure. (Leave plenty of space round each shape.)

1.

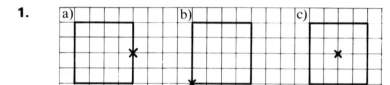

2.

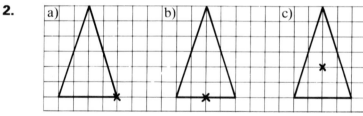

3.

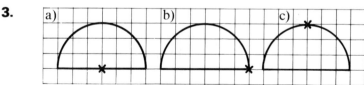

4.

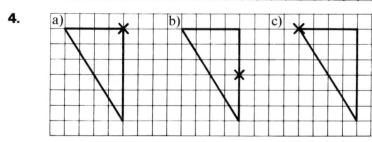

CONGRUENCE ════════════════════════════════════

Two shapes are congruent if they have exactly the same shape and size. One may have been turned over or round compared with the other.

Some examples of congruent shapes are

AA and MW and bd

EXERCISE 6f Look at these pairs of figures. Say whether or not the second figure is an exact copy of the first, although in a different position. If you are not sure, use tracing paper to help.

1.    **5.**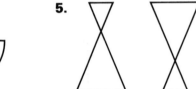

2. 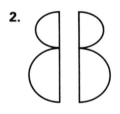   **6.**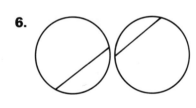

3. 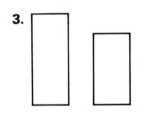   **7.**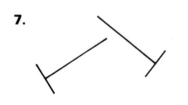

4.    **8.**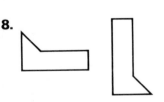

In each of the Questions 9 to 14 copy the whole diagram, Try to draw a line of symmetry to find out whether or not the given shapes are congruent.

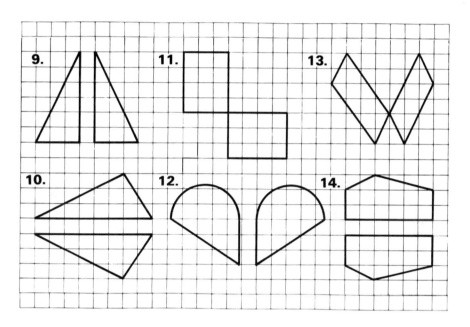

In Questions 15 to 18 use rotational symmetry to decide whether or not the given shapes are congruent.

15.

17.

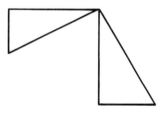

16.

18.

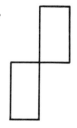

In Questions 19 to 27 find out whether or not the pairs of given shapes are congruent.

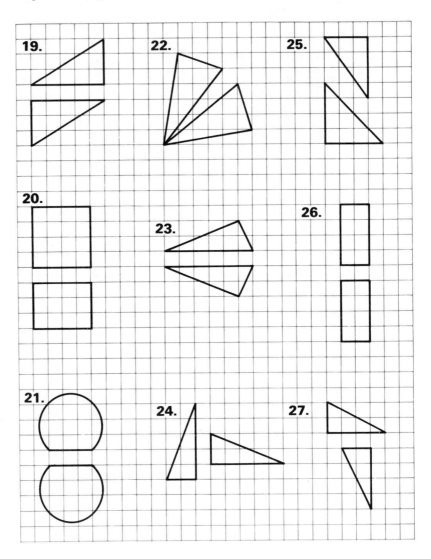

7 DECIMALS

DECIMAL NOTATION

The screw is being measured on a ruler graduated in centimetres and tenths of centimetres.

The length of this screw is 3 centimetres plus $\frac{3}{10}$ of a centimetre.

In decimal notation we write this as 3·3 cm.

This shows a ten-times magnification of the part of the ruler between 3·2 cm and 3·6 cm.

Each small division on the ruler is a hundredth of a centimetre.
We can now see that the length of the screw is 3·3 centimetres plus $\frac{1}{100}$ of a centimetre.

In decimal notation we write 3·31 cm.

The dot is called the decimal point.

The first number after the point means tenths
and its position is called the *first decimal place*.

The second number after the decimal point means hundredths
and its position is called the *second decimal place*.

EXERCISE 7a

> What is the value of the figure 5 in the number 12·45?
>
> 5 is in the second decimal place, so its value is $\frac{5}{100}$

1. What is the value of the figure 2 in each of the following numbers?

   a) 12·04   b) 36·21   c) 26·43   d) 50·52

2. What is the value of the figure 7 in each of the following numbers?

   a) 16·07   b) 3·7   c) 17   d) 24·71

3. What is the value of the figure 4 in each of the following numbers?

   a) 4·01   b) 14   c) 0·4   d) 0·04

4. Write the following numbers in order of size with the smallest first.

   2·25, 2·02, 2·2, 0·56.

   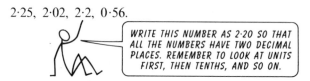

   WRITE THIS NUMBER AS 2·20 SO THAT ALL THE NUMBERS HAVE TWO DECIMAL PLACES. REMEMBER TO LOOK AT UNITS FIRST, THEN TENTHS, AND SO ON.

5. Write these numbers in order of size with the largest first.

   12·01, 10·3, 12·1, 21

6. Write these numbers in order of size with the smallest first.

   6·1, 3·79, 0·99, 1·06

7. From this set of numbers, {1·8, 4·03, 0·98, 9}, write down
   a) the largest number   b) the smallest number.

8. Write down the largest number and the smallest number from this list:

   16·8, 21·68, 5·3, 18·3, 0·79

9. What is the figure in the first decimal place in the number 15·45?

10. What is the value of the figure in the second decimal place in the number 20·34?

11. Write 12 and 5 tenths as a decimal number.

12. Write one and three tenths as a decimal number.

13. Write 1 and 2 tenths and 7 hundredths as a decimal number.

14. Write 2 tenths and 5 hundredths as a decimal number.

15. Use decimal notation to write the number thirty-one hundredths.

16. Use decimal notation to write down the number one and three hundredths.

17. Which of these two numbers are the same?

$$5·81, \ 51·8, \ 51·08, \ 51·80, \ 50·18$$

18. Which of these two numbers are the same?

$$65·07, \ 60·57, \ 6·57, \ 65·7, \ 657, \ 65·70$$

19. Write each of the following fractions in decimal notation.

a) $\frac{1}{10}$ c) $\frac{26}{100}$ e) $2\frac{3}{100}$

b) $\frac{5}{10}$ d) $5\frac{4}{10}$ f) $7\frac{31}{100}$

20. Write each of the following decimals as a fraction.

a) 0·27   c) 0·3   e) 1·07

b) 0·7   d) 1·7   f) 3·37

21. Write each of the following decimals as a fraction in its lowest terms.

a) 0·05   c) 0·48   e) 4·25

b) 0·75   d) 0·16   f) 12·5

ADDITION AND SUBTRACTION

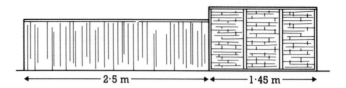

To find the total length of this fence we must add 2·5 m and 1·45 m.

This is easy if we write the numbers in columns:

$$\begin{array}{r} 2·50 \\ 1·45 \\ \hline 3·95 \end{array}$$

EXERCISE 7b

Find   25·08 − 9·4

$$\begin{array}{r} 25·08 \\ -\ 9·40 \\ \hline 15·68 \end{array}$$

REMEMBER TO KEEP THE DECIMAL POINTS IN LINE AND TO PUT A ZERO IN ANY "EMPTY" DECIMAL PLACE.

Find

1.	4·6 − 2·4	**13.**	0·5 − 0·12
2.	12·8 + 4·9	**14.**	3·8 + 4·6
3.	4·01 − 2·6	**15.**	13·8 + 1·22
4.	2·81 + 9·43	**16.**	24 − 1·9
5.	12·22 − 4·73	**17.**	0·5 − 0·02
6.	0·8 − 0·16	**18.**	3·6 + 0·07
7.	7·6 + 3·9	**19.**	5·1 + 1·95
8.	60·1 + 9·9	**20.**	10 − 4·9
9.	10 − 4·05	**21.**	3·62 + 0·78
10.	34·66 + 2·8	**22.**	5·8 − 1·92
11.	15 − 4·43	**23.**	8 − 1·52
12.	55·8 + 3·99	**24.**	4·63 + 1·37

25. $1·6 + 3·5 + 0·8$ **28.** $3·13 + 5·2 + 2·05$

26. $4 + 5·7 + 0·9$ **29.** $54 + 2·73 + 4·27$

27. $6·01 + 3·22 + 1·8$ **30.** $12·07 + 5·88 + 22·9$

31. This is an outline plan of a plot showing a new house.

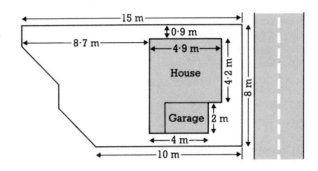

a) How long is the back wall of the house?
b) How far behind the front wall of the house is the front of the garage?
c) What is the distance between the outside garage wall and the edge of the plot?
d) How far is the front of the house from the front of the plot?

MEASUREMENT AND ACCURACY

It is not possible to measure anything exactly.

On this ruler, the end of the bolt is near the 2·2 mark.

As the end is nearer to 2·2 cm than to 2·1 cm, we can give its length as 2·2 cm to the nearest tenth of a centimere.

We write this as 2·2 cm correct to 1 dp. (dp is an abbreviation for "decimal place".)

This is a magnification of the scale showing hundredths of centimetres.

THE END OF THE BOLT IS NEARER
THE 2·17 MARK THAN THE 2·18 MARK.

Now we can see that the length of the bolt is 2·17 cm to the nearest hundredth of a centimetre. We write this as 2·17 cm correct to 2 dp.

> If the measurement appears to be exactly half-way
> between marks, round up.

EXERCISE 7c These diagrams show a magnification of a ruler graduated in centimetres.

Give each of the following measurements

a) to 2 dp (the nearest hundredth of a centimetre.)
b) to 1 dp (the nearest tenth of a centimetre.)

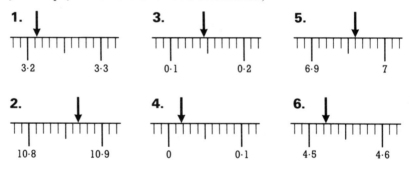

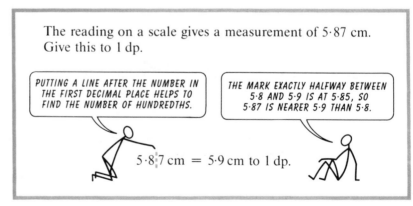

The reading on a scale gives a measurement of 5·87 cm. Give this to 1 dp.

PUTTING A LINE AFTER THE NUMBER IN
THE FIRST DECIMAL PLACE HELPS TO
FIND THE NUMBER OF HUNDREDTHS.

THE MARK EXACTLY HALFWAY BETWEEN
5·8 AND 5·9 IS AT 5·85, SO
5·87 IS NEARER 5·9 THAN 5·8.

5·8|7 cm = 5·9 cm to 1 dp.

Give the following quantities correct to 1 dp.

7.	8·56 cm	**13.**	8·04 mm	**19.**	4·85 kg
8.	4·58 m	**14.**	3·95 m	**20.**	36·22 m
9.	8·43 g	**15.**	32·08 mm	**21.**	17·98 cm
10.	6·69 mm	**16.**	8·94 g	**22.**	0·56 mm
11.	4·42 ℓ	**17.**	9·95 cm	**23.**	3·06 g
12.	12·25 cm	**18.**	23·02 mm	**24.**	8·69 m

Give the following numbers correct to 1 dp.

25. 7·34   **26.** 18·07   **27.** 4·16   **28.** 9·97

MULTIPLYING DECIMALS BY 10 AND 100

This pin is 1·4 cm long. ●—

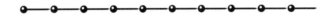

When ten of them are laid end to end, the length of the line can be found by adding ten lots of 1·4 cm.

This comes to 14 cm, so 1·4 × 10 = 14.

When we multiply by ten,

> the number of tenths becomes the number of units,
> and the number of units becomes the number of tens.

When we put this in headed columns, we can see the movement of the figures.

Tens	Units		Tenths	
	1	·	4	× 10
1	4	·	0	

Now we can see that, when we multiply by 10, the figures move one place to the left. This also happens when we multiply whole numbers by 10.

> When we multiply a number by 10,
> the figures move one place to the *left*.

If we lay 100 pins end to end, the line is   1·4 × 100 cm   long.

If we count up, we find that   1·4 × 100 = 140.

This time the figures have moved two places to the left, and again this also happens when we multiply whole numbers by 100.

> When we multiply a number by 100,
> the figures move two places to the *left*.

EXERCISE 7d

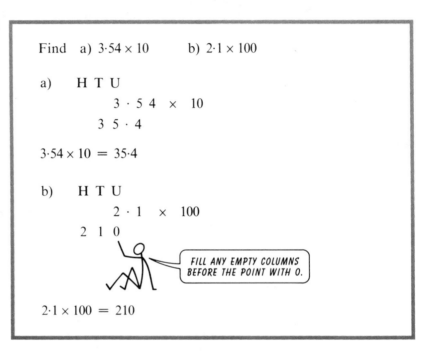

Find   a) 3·54 × 10   b) 2·1 × 100

a)   H T U

        3 · 5 4   ×   10

        3 5 · 4

3·54 × 10 = 35·4

b)   H T U

        2 · 1   ×   100

    2   1 0

FILL ANY EMPTY COLUMNS
BEFORE THE POINT WITH 0.

2·1 × 100 = 210

Find

1. 3·7 × 10	**5.** 34·4 × 10	**9.** 0·03 × 10
2. 1·6 × 10	**6.** 0·52 × 10	**10.** 16·42 × 10
3. 3·77 × 10	**7.** 1·05 × 10	**11.** 27 × 10
4. 0·8 × 10	**8.** 3 × 10	**12.** 250·54 × 10

13. 2·9 × 100	**17.** 24·8 × 100	**21.** 0·24 × 100
14. 7·2 × 100	**18.** 0·08 × 100	**22.** 6·1 × 100
15. 3·82 × 100	**19.** 2 × 100	**23.** 7 × 100
16. 0·14 × 100	**20.** 5·01 × 100	**24.** 16 × 100

25. $2·8 \times 10$ **27.** $0·59 \times 100$ **29.** 25×10

26. 12×100 **28.** $4·86 \times 10$ **30.** $0·8 \times 100$

DIVISION BY 10 AND BY 100

Division is the opposite of multiplication, so we move the figures the other way.

> To divide a number by 10,
> move the figures one place to the *right*.

> To divide a number by 100,
> move the figures two places to the *right*.

EXERCISE 7e

Find   a) $1·2 \div 10$ b) $75 \div 100$

a)   T U

         1 · 2   ÷ 10

         0 · 1 2

PUT O HERE TO SHOW THAT
THERE ARE NO UNITS.

$1·2 \div 10 = 0·12$

b)   T U

         7 5 ·   ÷ 100

         0 · 7 5

$75 \div 100 = 0·75$

Find

1. $24·6 \div 10$ **3.** $36·6 \div 10$ **5.** $5·8 \div 10$

2. $1·9 \div 10$ **4.** $53 \div 10$ **6.** $29 \div 10$

7. $24 \div 100$ **9.** $65 \div 100$ **11.** $4 \div 100$

8. $63 \div 100$ **10.** $8 \div 100$ **12.** $2.5 \div 100$

13.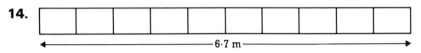

Each pin is 2·3 cm long.
How long is the line?

14.

How long is each paving slab?

15. There are 100 buttons in the box. Each button weighs 5·4 g.
What is the total weight of the buttons in the box?

16. There are 100 pencils in this box and their total weight is 950 g.
How much does each pencil weigh?

HB Pencils

USING A CALCULATOR FOR MULTIPLICATION

This pin is 0·8 cm long.

The length of three of them laid end to end is 3×0.8 cm.

Press $\boxed{3}\ \boxed{\times}\ \boxed{0}\ \boxed{\cdot}\ \boxed{8}\ \boxed{=}$

The display will show 2·4

So the length of the three pins is 2·4 cm.

EXERCISE 7f

Find $12 \cdot 6 \times 8$

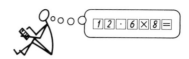

$12 \cdot 6 \times 8 = 100 \cdot 8$

Find

1. $2 \times 1 \cdot 4$	**5.** $2 \cdot 7 \times 14$	**9.** $2 \cdot 32 \times 56$
2. $4 \cdot 9 \times 4$	**6.** $26 \times 8 \cdot 4$	**10.** $32 \cdot 3 \times 2 \cdot 5$
3. $2 \cdot 7 \times 9$	**7.** $64 \times 18 \cdot 6$	**11.** $12 \cdot 2 \times 1 \cdot 6$
4. $32 \cdot 4 \times 12$	**8.** $28 \times 3 \cdot 67$	**12.** $53 \cdot 1 \times 0 \cdot 8$

13. a) Multiply 65 by $2 \cdot 4$. Is the answer bigger or smaller than 65?
b) Multiply 65 by some other numbers that are larger than 1. Are the answers bigger or smaller than 65?
c) Multiply 65 by $0 \cdot 3$. What do you notice about the size of the answer this time?
d) Multiply 65 by some other numbers that are less than 1. Does the same thing happen to the answer?

14. Investigate what happens to the number $0 \cdot 4$ when it is multiplied by

a) a number larger than 1
b) a number less than 1.

15. Each wall tile is $0 \cdot 4$ cm thick.
How high is a pile of 18 of these tiles?

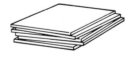

16. Each screw weighs $4 \cdot 8$ g. How heavy is a bag of 65 screws?

17. These paving stones are each 0·56 m long. 54 of them are laid end to end along a pavement. How long is the line of paving stones?

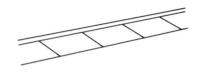

USING A CALCULATOR FOR DIVISION

This length of ribbon is 0·12 m.

It is cut into four equal lengths.

To find the length of one piece, we need to divide 0·12 by 4.

Press

The display gives 0·03.

Therefore each piece of ribbon is 0·03 m long.

EXERCISE 7g Find

1. 0·6 ÷ 2   **5.** 0·9 ÷ 9   **9.** 24·1 ÷ 2

2. 3·3 ÷ 2   **6.** 0·95 ÷ 5   **10.** 36 ÷ 0·9

3. 0·63 ÷ 3   **7.** 6·72 ÷ 3   **11.** 4·5 ÷ 0·9

4. 7·8 ÷ 3   **8.** 26·6 ÷ 14   **12.** 0·75 ÷ 5

13. The perimeter of this square is 14·6 m. How long is each side?

14. This block of cheese is to be divided into 80 portions. What does each portion weigh?

16·8 kg

15. A sack of flour weighs 28 kg.
The flour is shared equally amongst 5 people.
What weight of flour does each person get?

16. £36 is to be divided equally amongst 8 people.
How much does each person get?

GIVING APPROXIMATE ANSWERS

If we work out $3.79 \div 4.56$ on a calculator, the display fills up and looks something like this: 0.8311403

When this happens we have to decide how accurate we want the answer to be. If we want the answer correct to 1 decimal place, we write down the first *two* figures after the point.

$$3.74 \div 4.52 = 0.8|2 \ldots$$

> REMEMBER THE DOTTED LINE AFTER 1 dp.

$$= 0.8 \text{ correct to 1 dp}$$

If we want the answer correct to 2 decimal places, we write down the first *three* figures after the point.

$$3.74 \div 4.52 = 0.82|7$$

> THIS TIME THE DOTTED LINE GOES AFTER 2 dp.

$$= 0.83 \text{ correct to 2 dp}$$

EXERCISE 7h Giving your answers correct to 1 decimal place, find

1. $14.6 \div 7$ **2.** $6.15 \div 0.37$ **3.** $25 \div 13$

Giving your answers correct to 2 decimal places, find

4. $25.7 \div 0.29$ **5.** $8.3 \div 1.7$ **6.** $15 \div 27$

7. a) Divide 14·6 by 2·5. Is the answer bigger or smaller than 14·6?
   b) Divide 14·6 by some other numbers that are bigger than 1.
      Are the answers bigger or smaller than 14·6?
   c) Divide 14·6 by 0·3. What do you notice about the size of the
      answer this time?
   d) Divide 14·6 by some other numbers that are smaller than 1.
      Does the same thing happen to the answer as happened
      in (c)?

8. Investigate what happens to the number 0·3 when it is divided
   by
   a) a number larger than 1
   b) a number smaller than 1.

CHANGING FRACTIONS TO DECIMALS

The fraction $\frac{2}{5}$ can be thought of as $2 \div 5$.

Now $2 \div 5 = 0\cdot4$, therefore $\frac{2}{5} = 0\cdot4$.

> To change a fraction to a decimal, divide the top number
> (numerator) by the bottom number (denominator).

EXERCISE 7i Express the following fractions as decimals.

1. $\frac{1}{4}$ **3.** $\frac{3}{4}$ **5.** $\frac{4}{5}$

2. $\frac{3}{5}$ **4.** $\frac{1}{5}$ **6.** $\frac{1}{2}$

Some equivalent fractions and decimals are worth remembering:

$$\frac{1}{2} = 0\cdot5 \qquad \frac{1}{4} = 0\cdot25 \qquad \frac{3}{4} = 0\cdot75$$

Some fractions cannot be expressed exactly in decimal notation.
If you try to convert $\frac{2}{3}$ to a decimal, the display on your calculator
will fill up and look something like this: 0.6666666

When this happens, we have to decide how accurate we need the
answer to be. In this case, we will give the decimal to the nearest
hundredth, i.e. correct to two decimal places.

$$\frac{2}{3} = 0\cdot67 \text{ to 2 dp}$$

EXERCISE 7j

Express $\frac{2}{7}$ as a decimal correct to 1 dp.

$2 \div 7 =$

WRITE DOWN THE FIRST
TWO DECIMAL PLACES
IF THE ANSWER IS TO
BE CORRECT TO 1dp.

$$\frac{2}{7} = 0\cdot2\,|\,8\ldots$$

$$= 0\cdot3 \text{ correct to 1 dp}$$

Express the following fractions as decimals correct to 1 dp.

1. $\frac{2}{9}$ **4.** $\frac{9}{11}$ **7.** $\frac{4}{15}$

2. $\frac{1}{12}$ **5.** $\frac{3}{7}$ **8.** $\frac{6}{7}$

3. $\frac{5}{7}$ **6.** $\frac{2}{11}$ **9.** $\frac{4}{33}$

Express the following fractions as decimals correct to 2 dp.

10. $\frac{3}{19}$ **15.** $\frac{2}{13}$

11. $\frac{1}{3}$ **16.** $\frac{5}{6}$

THIS TIME WRITE DOWN
THE FIRST THREE DECIMAL
PLACES ON THE DISPLAY.

12. $\frac{7}{15}$ **17.** $\frac{5}{8}$

13. $\frac{1}{6}$ **18.** $\frac{2}{21}$

14. $\frac{4}{7}$ **19.** $\frac{7}{11}$

Which is bigger, 0.7 or $\frac{7}{9}$?

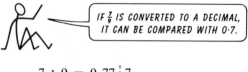

IF $\frac{7}{9}$ IS CONVERTED TO A DECIMAL, IT CAN BE COMPARED WITH 0·7.

$$7 \div 9 = 0.77 \vdots 7$$
$$= 0.78 \text{ correct to 2 dp}$$
$$\text{and} \quad 0.7 = 0.70$$

So $\frac{7}{9}$ is bigger than 0.7.

20. Which is bigger, 0.6 or $\frac{4}{7}$?

21. Which is smaller, 0.3 or $\frac{2}{11}$?

22. Write these numbers in order of size with the smallest first.

$$\frac{2}{5}, \ 0.6, \ \frac{1}{3}$$

23. Write these numbers in order of size with the largest first.

$$\frac{3}{4}, \ 0.8, \ \frac{5}{7}$$

MIXED EXERCISES

EXERCISE 7k **1.** Find $6.43 \div 0.7$ correct to 2 decimal places.

2. Add 4.5, 6.87 and 2.3 together.

3. Express 0.64 as a fraction in its lowest terms.

4. Find 0.5×18.

5. Multiply 4.8 by 100.

6. Divide 38 by 10.

EXERCISE 7l **1.** Which is larger, 0·9 or $\frac{7}{8}$?

2. Which of these numbers is the smallest?

$$0·4, \frac{1}{4}, 0·3.$$

3. Multiply 4·25 by 10.

4. Divide 50·3 by 10.

5. Find 23·1 ÷ 2·7 correct to 2 decimal places.

6. Take 1·8 away from 6·59.

EXERCISE 7m **1.** Add 51·5, 30·5, and 2·66 together.

2. Express 0·45 as a fraction in its lowest terms.

3. Write $\frac{4}{7}$ as a decimal correct to 2 decimal places.

4. Divide 12 by 100.

5. Subtract 3·58 from 8·7.

6. Which of these numbers is the largest?

$$0·6, \frac{2}{3}, \frac{5}{8}$$

8 TRIANGLES

THE SUM OF THE ANGLES IN A TRIANGLE

EXERCISE 8a **1.** On a piece of firm paper draw a large triangle of any shape. Each side should be longer than your protractor. Mark the angles A, B and C.

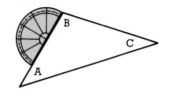

2. Place the centre of your protractor on one corner and draw round the curved edge of the protractor as shown in the diagram.
Do this for each of the other two corners.

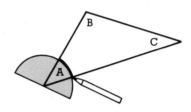

3. Cut out the triangle and cut each corner off following the curve you have drawn.

Lay the three corners along the edge of your ruler. They should look like this

THE THREE ANGLES FIT TOGETHER TO MAKE A STRAIGHT LINE.

We know that the angles on a straight line add up to 180° so now we have shown that

the three angles of a triangle add up to 180°.

82

EXERCISE 8b **1.** a) Draw a triangle with sides longer than 5 cm.
   b) For each angle decide whether it is acute or obtuse and then measure it.
   c) Add the three angles together.
   d) Do they add up to 180° – or very nearly?

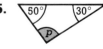

IF YOU DON'T GET ABOUT 180°, CHECK EACH ANGLE AGAIN. MAKE CERTAIN THAT YOU USE THE RIGHT SCALE.

2. Repeat Question 1 with a triangle of a different shape.

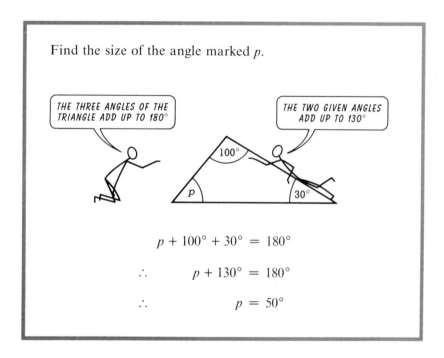

Find the size of the angle marked *p*.

THE THREE ANGLES OF THE TRIANGLE ADD UP TO 180°

THE TWO GIVEN ANGLES ADD UP TO 130°

$$p + 100° + 30° = 180°$$

$$\therefore \quad p + 130° = 180°$$

$$\therefore \quad p = 50°$$

In each triangle find the size of the angle marked *p*.

3.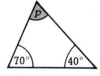

4.

5.

6.   **7.**   **8.**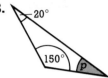

EQUILATERAL TRIANGLES

In an equilateral triangle, all sides have the same length.

EXERCISE 8c   Copy this equilateral triangle onto thin tracing paper.

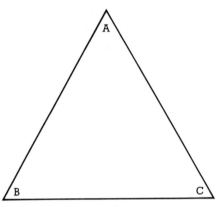

1.   Lay it on the triangle in the book so that the angle marked A is over the angle marked B.

a) Do the triangles fit?

Turn your triangle round until A is over C.

b) Do the triangles fit?

c) What kind of symmetry does this show an equilateral triangle to have?

d) What do you think this means about the size of each angle?

2.   Fold your triangle in half.

a) Do the two halves fit exactly?

Open your triangle and draw a line along the fold.

b) Is this a line of symmetry?

c) Are there any more lines of symmetry in an equilateral triangle?

> In an equilateral triangle, all three sides are the same length and all three angles are 60°.

ISOSCELES TRIANGLES

An isosceles triangle has two equal sides.

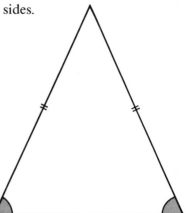

EXERCISE 8d **1.** Two of the sides of this triangle are equal. To show which sides are equal, they are marked with two small dashes.

    a) Measure the two shaded angles.

    b) What do you notice?

2. Repeat Question 1 for each of these triangles.

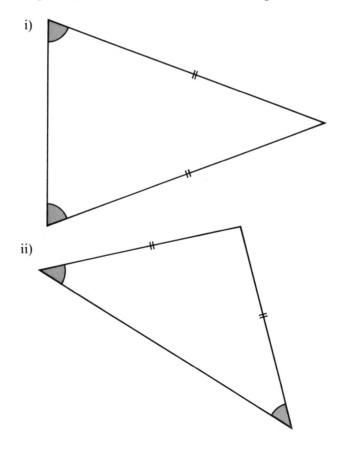

i)

ii)

A triangle with two equal sides and two equal angles
is called an *isosceles triangle*.

The equal angles are at the ends of the *base* of the triangle.
We call the "odd side out" the "base", but it is not always at the
bottom.

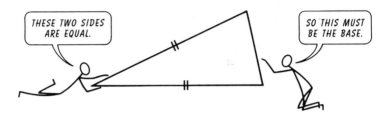

EXERCISE 8e

Find the size of the angles marked a and b.

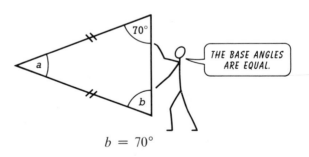

$$b = 70°$$

The angles in the triangle add up to 180°.

$$\therefore \quad a + b + 70° = 180°$$

$$\therefore \quad a + 70° + 70° = 180°$$

$$\text{i.e.} \quad a + 140° = 180°$$

$$\therefore \quad a = 40°$$

Find the size of each marked angle.

1.

4.

7.

2.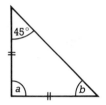

5.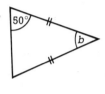

8.

3.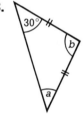

6.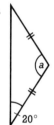

9.

MIXED EXERCISE

EXERCISE 8f   1.   Find the size of the angle marked A.

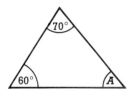

2. This is an isosceles triangle. Copy it and shade two equal angles.

3. Triangle PQR is an isosceles triangle. (A triangle can be named by the three letters at its vertices.)

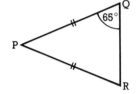

   a) Copy the triangle.
   b) If there is a line of symmetry, draw it.
   c) Find the size of the angle at P.

Find the size of each shaded angle.

4.
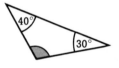

7.
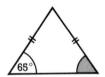

10.

5.
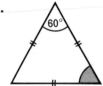

8.
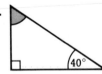

11.
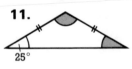

6.
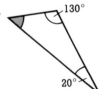

9.

12.
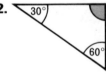

9 WHOLE NUMBERS 3

MULTIPLES

So far in this book, when we have talked about numbers we have been dealing with calculations. Now we need to look at the numbers themselves and see how they are constructed.

This is part of a multiplication table.

×	1	2	3	4	5	6	7	8	9	...
1	1	2	3	4	5	6	7	8	9	...
2	2	4	6	8	10	12	14	16	18	...
3	3	6	9	12	15	18	21	24	27	...
4	4	8	12	16	20	24	28	32	36	...
5	5	10	15	20	25	30	35	40	45	...

THESE ARE MULTIPLES OF 5.

The numbers in the 5th row are all *multiples* of 5.

$$30 = 6 \times 5, \qquad 45 = 9 \times 5.$$

There are other multiples as well as these such as

$$125 \ (25 \times 5) \qquad \text{and} \qquad 80 \ (16 \times 5).$$

Any number multiplied by 5 gives an answer which is a multiple of 5.

Notice that we can write 30 as 5×6 or as 6×5 because these are the same.

EXERCISE 9a Use your calculator as little as possible in this chapter.

1. Make your own 12×12 multiplication table.

2. From the table, give four multiples of 4.

3. How many different multiples of 3 are there in the table?

4. From the table, give four multiples of 8.

5. Give a multiple of 3 which is not in the table.

6. Is 48 a multiple of 6?

7. Is 60 a multiple of 4?

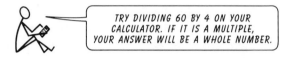

TRY DIVIDING 60 BY 4 ON YOUR CALCULATOR. IF IT IS A MULTIPLE, YOUR ANSWER WILL BE A WHOLE NUMBER.

8. Is 24 a multiple of 7?

9. Add two more numbers to this number pattern.

7, 14, 21 ...

10. 72 pence are to be shared equally amongst 9 children.
a) Is 72 a multiple of 9?
b) When the money is shared out, will there be any left over?

EXERCISE 9b **1.** Write down five *even* numbers (i.e. multiples of 2).

2. Is 456 an even number? How do you recognise an even number? Is 7658 an even number?

3. An *odd* number is any number that is not an even number, so 5 and 19 are odd numbers.
a) Give three odd numbers that are less than 10.
b) Give three odd numbers between 20 and 30.

4. How can you recognise a multiple of a) 10   b) 5?

5. Which of the following numbers are multiples of 5?

25, 75, 53, 20, 5

6. Which of the following numbers are multiples of 10?

60, 100, 104, 35

EXERCISE 9c

a) Is 30 a multiple of 10?

b) Is 17 a multiple of 5?

MULTIPLES OF 10 END IN 0,
MULTIPLES OF 5 END IN 5 OR 0.

a) 30 is a multiple of 10.

b) 17 is not a multiple of 5.

1. Is 35 a multiple of 5?

2. Which of the following numbers are multiples of 10?

45, 20, 100, 75

3. $13 \times 4 = 52$ so 52 is a multiple of 4. Give another multiple of 4 which is greater than 8.

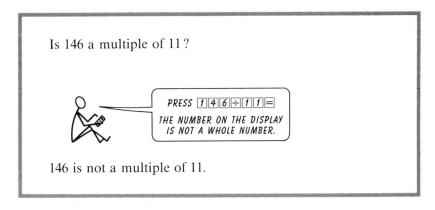

Is 146 a multiple of 11?

PRESS $\boxed{1}\boxed{4}\boxed{6}\boxed{\div}\boxed{1}\boxed{1}\boxed{=}$

THE NUMBER ON THE DISPLAY IS NOT A WHOLE NUMBER.

146 is not a multiple of 11.

4. Is 45 a multiple of 7?

5. Is 243 a multiple of 3?

6. Is 438 a multiple of 9?

7. Is 92 a multiple of 8?

8. a) Is 182 a multiple of 7 ?

b) A group of 182 people is being divided into teams of 7. Will anyone not be in a team ?

9. a) List, starting with 25, the first five multiples of 25.

b)

Each bus will seat 25 people. 120 people want to go on an outing.

So as not to lose money, each bus that is hired must be full.

How many people can be allowed to go on the outing ? (There are four possibilities.)

c) If enough coaches are hired to take everybody, how many empty seats will there be ?

FACTORS

$15 = 5 \times 3$ and we say that 5 and 3 are *factors* of 15.

$24 = 4 \times 6$ or 3×8 or 2×12

so 2, 3, 4, 6, 8 and 12 are factors of 24.

$24 = 1 \times 24$ too, so 1 and 24 are also factors of 24.

IF YOU WRITE 24 AS 2×12, YOU ARE WRITING 24 AS THE *PRODUCT* OF TWO FACTORS.

A *FACTOR* OF 24 WILL DIVIDE INTO 24 EXACTLY, LEAVING NO REMAINDER.

EXERCISE 9d

a) Is 10 a factor of 35 ?

b) Is 5 a factor of 75 ?

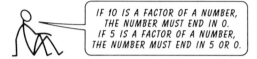

IF 10 IS A FACTOR OF A NUMBER,
THE NUMBER MUST END IN 0.
IF 5 IS A FACTOR OF A NUMBER,
THE NUMBER MUST END IN 5 OR 0.

a) 10 is not a factor of 35.

b) 5 is a factor of 75.

1. a) Give 6 as the product of two factors in two different ways.
b) Now write down all the factors of 6.

2. a) Write 20 as the product of two factors in as many ways as you can. (There are three ways.)
b) Now write down all the factors of 20. (You should find 6 factors.)

3. Write down all the factors of 36.

4. Is 5 a factor of   a) 25   b) 17   c) 325 ?

5. Write down all the factors of   a) 18   b) 16.

6. Write down all the factors of   a) 11   b) 13   c) 17.
What do you notice about the number of factors ?

7. Find a number that is a factor of both 24 and 21.

8. Find the biggest number that is a factor of both 24 and 18.

9. Write down all the factors of 64.

10. Find the biggest number that is a factor of both 12 and 24.

PRIME NUMBERS

A prime number is a number which can only be written as
1 × itself.

19 = 1 × 19   and this is the only way of writing 19 in factors,
so 19 is a prime number.

24 has many factors so it is not a prime number.

1 is a special number. It has no factors except 1 itself.
It is *not* a prime number.

EXERCISE 9e

Is 27 a prime number?

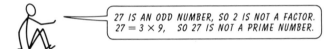

27 IS AN ODD NUMBER, SO 2 IS NOT A FACTOR.
27 = 3 × 9,   SO 27 IS NOT A PRIME NUMBER.

27 is not a prime number.

1. Check all the whole numbers less than 10 and list the prime
numbers you find. (You should find four.)

2. List the prime numbers between 10 and 20.

3. Is 26 a prime number?

4. Write down all the factors of 48.
Which of these are prime numbers?

5. Write down all the factors of 35.
Which of these are prime numbers?

6. a) Is 2 a factor of 29?
   b) Find out whether any of the prime numbers listed in
      Question 1 are factors of 29. (Test them in order of size to
      avoid missing any.)
   c) Is 29 a prime number?

7. Use the method of Question 6 to find out whether 41 and 51 are prime numbers.

8. List all the prime numbers between 20 and 30.

9. Draw a ten-by-ten number square, showing the numbers from 1 to 100. Ring all the prime numbers.

10. Find the sum of the first 3 prime numbers.

11. What is the difference between the fourth prime number and the fifth prime number?

12. Find the number obtained when the second prime number is multiplied by the fourth prime number.

PRIME FACTORS

Numbers which are not prime can be written as the product of prime numbers.

For example, $15 = 3 \times 5$

and $20 = 4 \times 5$

$$= 2 \times 2 \times 5$$

Remember that 1 is a special number and doesn't follow the same rules.

EXERCISE 9f

Find the number $2 \times 2 \times 2 \times 3$

$2 \times 2 \times 2 \times 3 = 4 \times 2 \times 3$

$= 8 \times 3$

$= 24$

OR PRESS

$\boxed{2}\boxed{\times}\boxed{2}\boxed{\times}\boxed{2}\boxed{\times}\boxed{3}\boxed{=}$

Find the following numbers.

1. $2 \times 2 \times 3$ **3.** $2 \times 3 \times 11$ **5.** 2×7

2. $2 \times 3 \times 5$ **4.** $3 \times 3 \times 7$ **6.** $2 \times 7 \times 7$

7.

Out of the numbers 2, 3 and 7 we can build other numbers, by multiplying.

We can build 14 from 2×7, and 63 from $3 \times 3 \times 7$.

a) Build four more numbers out of 2, 3 and 7.
b) Notice that you can use just one prime number several times. Find $7 \times 7 \times 7$ and $2 \times 2 \times 2 \times 2$.
c) Build two more numbers like those in (b).

Write 45 as the product of prime numbers.

$45 = 5 \times 9$

$\quad = 5 \times 3 \times 3$

PUT THE FACTORS IN SIZE ORDER.

$\quad = 3 \times 3 \times 5$

Write each of the following numbers as the product of prime factors, in size order.

8. 14	**11.** 16	**14.** 33
9. 4	**12.** 36	**15.** 35
10. 10	**13.** 28	**16.** 42

MIXED EXERCISES

EXERCISE 9g **1.** Copy and complete the following sentence.

6 is a _____ of 12.

2. Build three numbers less than 20, by multiplying, out of the prime numbers 2 and 3. Each prime number may be used as often as you like or you need not use it at all.

3. Is 54 a multiple of 8?

4. Find the biggest factor of both 20 and 25.

5. Is 17 a prime number?

EXERCISE 9h **1.** Give two multiples of 5.

2. Give two factors of 24.

3. Name the next prime number after 5.

4. Work out the value of $2 \times 3 \times 5$.

5. Is 19 a prime number?

EXERCISE 9i **1.** Is 6 a factor of 18 or is 6 a multiple of 18?

2. Is 33 a prime number?

3. Write 21 as the product of prime numbers.

4. 18 is a multiple of 9. Give the next multiple of 9.

5. Is this statement true or false?
"The factors of 15 are 1, 3 and 15."
If it is false, write a correct version.

10 SHAPES AND TESSELLATIONS

THE PARALLELOGRAM

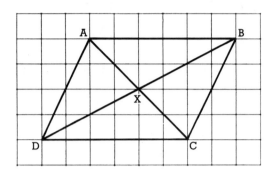

This is a parallelogram. Its opposite sides are parallel. AC and BD are diagonals. (We can name a line by the two letters at the ends.) They intersect at X.

If the parallelogram is rotated about X through 180°, it will look the same. We say that the parallelogram has rotational symmetry of order 2.

EXERCISE 10a **1.** Copy the parallelogram ABCD. Now draw the parallelogram again when it has been turned about X by 180°.
Label your second diagram using the letters A, B, C and D in their new positions.

2. What do your diagrams tell you about

a) the lengths of AB and CD
b) the lengths of AD and BC
c) the lengths of AX and XC
d) the lengths of BX and XD?

3. Repeat Question 1 but this time do not draw the diagonals. (The diagonals are the lines joining A to C and B to D.)

What do your diagrams tell you about the size of

a) the angles at A and at C
b) the angles at B and at D
c) the angles at A and at D?

98

The results from the previous exercise suggest that for any parallelogram,

the opposite sides are equal and parallel

the diagonals bisect each other

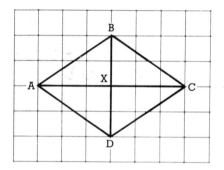

"BISECT" MEANS "DIVIDE INTO TWO EQUAL PARTS".

the opposite angles are equal.

THE RHOMBUS

A parallelogram with four equal sides is called a *rhombus*. A rhombus has the shape of a diamond.

EXERCISE 10b 1. Copy the rhombus ABCD.
  a) Place a mirror along AC. Is AC a line of symmetry?
  b) Place a mirror along BD. Is BD a line of symmetry?
  c) Can you place the mirror in any other position to get a line of symmetry?

  2. What can you say about
  a) the lengths of AX and XC
  b) the lengths of BX and XD?

  3. What can you say about
  a) the sum of the four angles at X
  b) the size of each of the angles at X?

A rhombus has all the properties of a parallelogram. In addition:

any two adjacent sides are equal

"ADJACENT" MEANS
"NEXT TO ONE ANOTHER".

the diagonals of a rhombus cut each other in half
at right angles

the diagonals are lines of symmetry.

THE KITE

This is a kite.

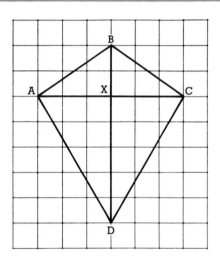

EXERCISE 10c **1.** a) Place a mirror along AC. Is AC a line of symmetry?
b) Place a mirror along BD. Is BD a line of symmetry?
c) Can you place the mirror in any other position to get a line of symmetry?

2. What can you say about

a) the lengths of AX and XC
b) the lengths of BX and XD?

3. What can you say about

a) the sum of the four angles at X
b) the size of each of the angles at X?

A kite has:
one line of symmetry,
one pair of opposite angles equal
two pairs of adjacent sides equal.

EXERCISE 10d State whether each of the following shapes is a square, a rectangle, a parallelogram, a rhombus or a kite. If it is none of these, write "general quadrilateral".

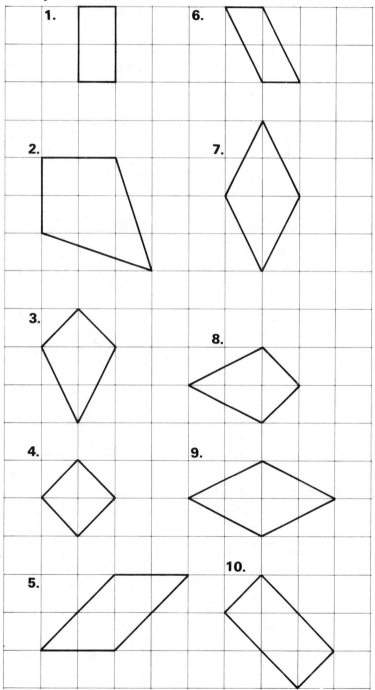

TESSELLATIONS

In Book 1B we found that square tiles and rectangular tiles would tessellate, i.e. tiles with these shapes could be used to cover a kitchen floor and would do so without gaps. In this chapter we are going to look at other shapes that tessellate.

If we cut a square tile in half from corner to corner we get two equal triangular tiles. As the square tiles tessellate, the triangular tiles also tessellate. For example

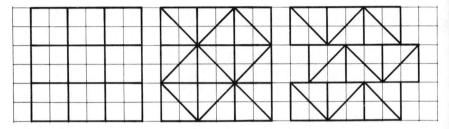

Any right-angled, triangular tile will tessellate because when two such tiles are put together they form a rectangle, and all rectangles tessellate.

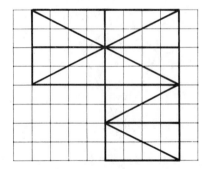

EXERCISE 10e In Questions 1 to 4 name each shape and then using squared paper show whether or not each shape can be used to tile a floor. Show the position of at least six tiles.

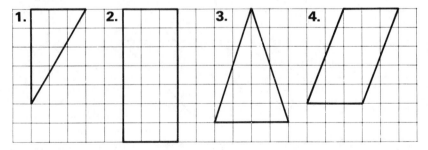

In Questions 5 to 8 name each shape, then use dotted paper to show whether or not each shape can be used to tile a floor. Show at least six tiles.

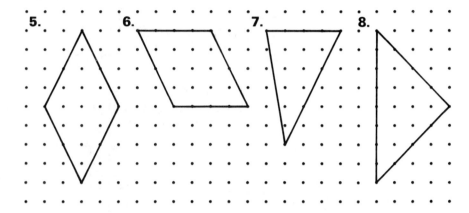

9. Can you find a triangular tile that does not tessellate?

Draw several triangular tile patterns to help you to answer this question.

Do all triangular tiles tessellate?

10. Copy each design onto squared paper and extend the pattern by adding at least four more tiles.

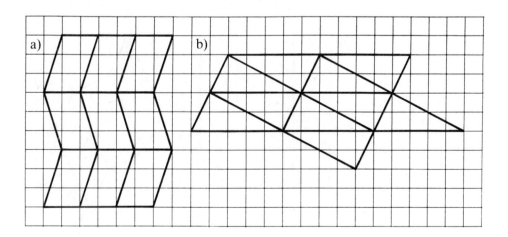

11. Design a tiling pattern for each of these shapes.

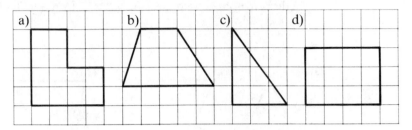

12. Copy each design onto squared paper and extend the pattern by adding at least six more tiles.

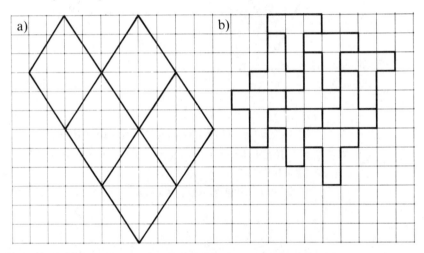

13. These tiling patterns are made with tiles of two different shapes. Copy each design onto squared paper and extend the pattern by adding at least six more tiles.

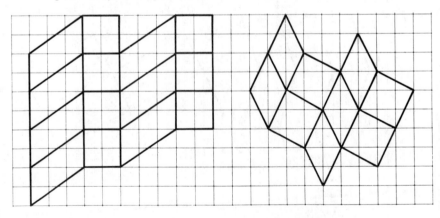

11 NEGATIVE NUMBERS

TEMPERATURE

When you listen to a weather forecast you will usually hear the announcer giving temperatures in degrees Celsius (or centigrade). The temperature is found by reading a thermometer.

On a hot summer day the temperature might be about 30 °C, i.e. 30 °Celsius.

Water freezes at a temperature of 0 °C.

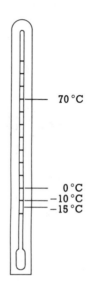

70 °C

When it is even colder than this, the temperature goes *below zero*.

On a day when the temperature is 10° below zero the reading on the thermometer is −10. We say that the temperature is *minus 10 °C* or *negative 10 °C*. If it gets even colder, and the thermometer gives a reading of −15, we see that the temperature is 15 °C below zero.

0 °C
−10 °C
−15 °C

Although temperatures below zero are given as negative numbers, we do not have to put a positive sign in front of a temperature that is above zero, i.e. 5 is the same as +5.

7 °C is 7 degrees above zero.

−7 °C is 7 degrees below zero.

EXERCISE 11a Write down, in words, the meaning of the following temperatures.

1. −4 °C   **3.** −11 °C   **5.** 26 °C

2. 8 °C   **4.** −1 °C   **6.** 14 °C

7. Here is a diagram of a thermometer.

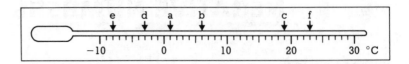

Write down each of the temperatures marked a, b, c, d, e and f, using a positive or a negative number.

8. Which is colder, $-5\,°C$ or $-9\,°C$?

9. Is $3\,°C$ higher or lower than $-4\,°C$?

10. Is $2\,°C$ higher or lower than $-2\,°C$?

Write down the higher temperature in each pair.

11. $11\,°C,\ 9\,°C$ **14.** $-3\,°C,\ -7\,°C$

12. $2\,°C,\ -5\,°C$ **15.** $-6\,°C,\ 1\,°C$

13. $-1\,°C,\ 6\,°C$ **16.** $0\,°C,\ -8\,°C$

17. Copy the part of a thermometer given below and mark these temperatures on it. The first one is done for you.

a) $8\,°C$ b) $-6\,°C$ c) $-1\,°C$ d) $4\,°C$ e) $0\,°C$

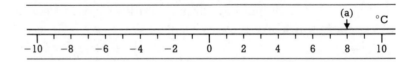

18. Write down all the temperatures given in Question 17 that are below zero.

19. Which is the lowest temperature of those given in Question 17?

20. Write down the temperatures given in Question 17 in order of increasing temperature, i.e. with the lowest first.

HEIGHT

The height of a cliff, a hill or a mountain is given as a number of metres *above sea-level*, e.g. Ben Nevis is 1342 m above sea-level.

If we stand on the beach, our height above sea-level is zero.

A shark swimming ten metres *under* the surface of the sea is *below sea-level* so we write its position compared with the surface as −10 m.

This diagram shows the position compared with sea-level of several objects.

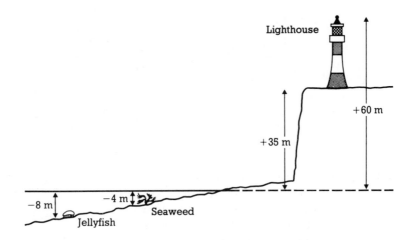

EXERCISE 11b Using positive numbers for "above sea-level" and negative numbers for "below sea-level", write down the position compared with sea-level of each of the following objects.

1. A rock climber who is 60 m up a cliff face.

2. An aircraft flying at 8000 m.

3. A submarine submerged at 100 m .

4. A child paddling at the edge of the sea.

5. A wreck on the sea-bed at a depth of 700 m.

6. Copy this contour map (your copy need not be exact). Shade the part of the map that is below sea level. Using a different colour, shade the highest part.

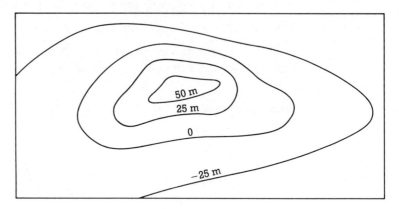

Whenever a quantity can go above or below a particular position (i.e. a zero level) we can state where it is by using positive and negative numbers.

EXERCISE 11c In the Grand Hotel there are ten floors above the ground floor, a lower ground floor, a basement and a sub-basement. These are shown in the diagram.

1. Taking the ground floor as zero, what is the number of

    a) the eighth floor above the ground floor

    b) the basement

    c) the top floor

    d) the lower ground floor?

2. Which floor has the number -2?

3. What is the number of the floor seven floors below floor 5?

4. What is the number of the floor five floors above floor -3?

5. What is the number of the floor four floors below floor 3?

6. What is the number of the floor three floors below floor 1?

7. What is the number of the floor ten floors above floor −2?

8. What is the number of the floor two floors above floor 0?

9. What is the number of the floor eight floors below floor 7?

10. What is the number of the floor five floors below floor 2?

In Questions 11 to 14, take as zero the moment when a rocket is launched. Give times using positive or negative numbers.

11. Write down the time
    a) ten seconds before launch,
    b) five seconds after launch.

12. Describe in words what times are meant by
    a) −1 second,   b) +8 seconds.

13. It is now 10 seconds after lift-off.
    a) What time was it 20 seconds ago?
    b) What time will it be after another 30 seconds?

14. It is now 5 seconds before lift-off.
    a) What time will it be in 2 seconds?
    b) What time will it be in 7 seconds?

GETTING WARMER

Suppose that when you get up one morning the temperature is 15°C. The temperature then rises and by lunchtime it is five degrees warmer.

The thermometer now shows 20°C.

$$15 + 5 = 20$$

Now look at what happens on a cold day.

At nine o'clock the temperature is −2°C. By noon it has gone up by eight degrees. The thermometer now shows 6°C.

$$-2 + 8 = 6$$

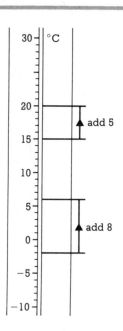

If the temperature starts at −10 °C and then goes up by seven degrees, it is still 3 °C below zero, i.e. −3 °C.

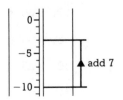

$$-10 + 7 = -3$$

This shows that, even after it has risen, the temperature may still be below zero.

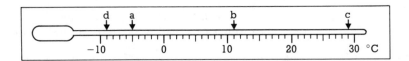

When the temperature goes *up* we *add*.

EXERCISE 11d Use this drawing of a thermometer to answer Questions 1 to 7.

1. Write down the temperatures marked a, b, c and d.

2. What temperature is 5 degrees higher than 3 °C?

3. What temperature is 5 degrees higher than −3 °C?

4. What temperature is 2 degrees higher than 8 °C?

5. What temperature is 2 degrees higher than −8 °C?

6. The temperature goes up from 5 °C to 16 °C. By how many degrees has it risen?

7. The temperature goes from −15 °C to −9 °C.
a) Has the temperature fallen or risen?
b) By how many degrees has the temperature changed?

8. The temperature has changed from 10 °C to −6 °C.
a) Has the temperature fallen or risen?
b) By how many degrees has the temperature changed?

The temperature starts at $-8\,°C$ and goes up by 5 degrees. Write an addition to show that the new temperature is $-3\,°C$.

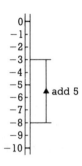

$$-8 + 5 = -3$$

Write an addition for each question from 9 to 12.

9.   **10.**   **11.**   **12.**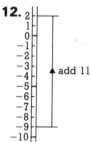

Draw a diagram for each addition given in Questions 13 to 16.

13. $-3 + 7 = 4$ **15.** $-6 + 3 = -3$

14. $-9 + 4 = -5$ **16.** $-7 + 9 = 2$

GETTING COLDER

Suppose that one afternoon the temperature is $21\,°C$ and by evening it has fallen by 6 degrees to a temperature of $15\,°C$. We can write

$$21 - 6 = 15$$

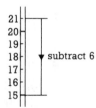

Similarly, if on a frosty evening the temperature falls by 5 degrees from 3 °C to −2 °C, we can write

$$3 - 5 = -2$$

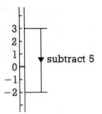

In Scotland the night temperature might fall by 10 degrees from −1 °C to −11 °C, i.e.

$$-1 - 10 = -11$$

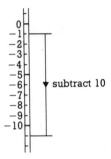

When the temperature *falls* we *subtract*.

EXERCISE 11e Use this drawing of part of a thermometer to answer Questions 1 to 6.

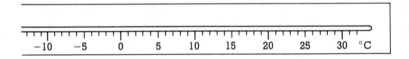

1. What temperature is 4 degrees lower than 7 °C?

2. What temperature is 4 degrees lower than −7 °C?

3. What temperature is 9 degrees lower than 6 °C?

4. What temperature is 5 degrees lower than −6 °C?

5. The temperature goes from 19 °C to 4 °C.
   By how many degrees has it fallen?

6. The temperature goes from −2 °C to −12 °C.
   a) Has the temperature risen or fallen?
   b) By how many degrees has the temperature changed?

The temperature starts at 3 °C and goes down by 11 degrees. Write a subtraction to show that the new temperature is −8 °C.

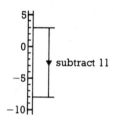

$$3 - 11 = -8$$

Write a subtraction for each question from 7 to 10.

7.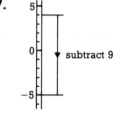

9.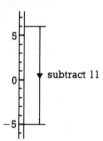

8.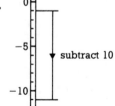

10.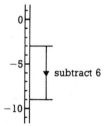

Draw a diagram for each subtraction given in Questions 11 to 14.

11. $7 - 10 = -3$

13. $-2 - 5 = -7$

12. $-1 - 10 = -11$

14. $9 - 20 = -11$

USING POSITIVE AND NEGATIVE NUMBERS

Many of the problems about temperature that we have been doing depended upon reading the scale on a thermometer. The scale was made up of both positive and negative numbers.

Suppose now that we draw the scale only, using the same positive and negative numbers but no longer thinking of them as degrees. All we have this time is a line of numbers. It is called a *number line.*

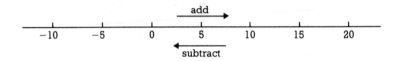

We can add and subtract numbers just as we did with temperatures.

EXERCISE 11f Use this number line to answer the questions below.

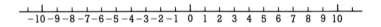

What number is given when −4 is

a) increased by 10   b) decreased by 3 ?

a) −4 + 10 = 6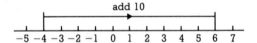

b) −4 − 3 = −7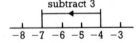

Write down the greater of each pair of numbers.

1. 2, −5   **3.** −1, −7   **5.** 0, −6

2. −3, 3   **4.** 8, −9   **6.** −2, 1

7. Starting with 6, what number is given by

a) an increase of 8   b) a decrease of 8?

8. Starting with −3, what number is given by

a) a decrease of 5   b) an increase of 3?

Draw a number line from −10 to 10. Illustrate on your line each of the following statements.

a) −1 − 4 = −5   b) −7 + 12 = 5

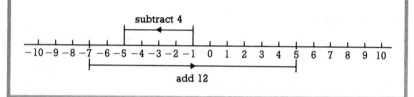

For each question from 9 to 15 draw a number line and use it to illustrate the given statements. (Use a different colour for each part of the question if you can.)

9. a) 4 − 7 = −3   b) −2 − 3 = −5

10. a) −3 + 9 = 6   b) −7 + 7 = 0

11. a) 2 − 5 = −3   b) 6 − 9 = −3

12. a) −9 + 7 = −2   b) −6 + 14 = 8

13. a) −1 − 3 = −4   b) −2 + 8 = 6

14. a) −5 + 4 = −1   b) 7 − 8 = −1

15. a) 6 − 5 = 1   b) 5 − 11 = −6

Copy each statement and fill in the missing number.

16. a) 7 − 9 = $\boxed{-2}$ b) −2 − 6 = $\boxed{-8}$

17. a) 3 − 5 = $\boxed{-2}$ b) −1 + $\boxed{5}$ = 4

18. a) 4 − $\boxed{6}$ = −2   b) $\boxed{5}$ − 3 = 2

19. a) $\boxed{-2}$ + 4 = 2   b) −7 + 9 = $\boxed{2}$

20. a) $-7 - 5 =$ ⬚$\text{-}12$ b) $4 -$ ⬚9 $= -5$

21. a) $-2 +$ ⬚7 $= 5$ b) $-6 - 6 =$ ⬚$\text{-}12$

22. a) ⬚$\text{-}2$ $- 4 = -6$ b) $2 -$ ⬚10 $= -8$

23. a) $-1 -$ ⬚4 $= -5$ b) $-1 +$ ⬚6 $= 5$

MIXED EXERCISE

EXERCISE 11g In this picture of a swimming pool the rungs of the ladder up to the diving board have numbers on them and so have the rungs on the ladder going down into the water.

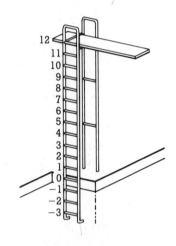

Use these numbers to answer Questions 1 to 5.

1. Sanjit climbs down 8 rungs from the top of the diving board.
On which rung is he now standing?

2. Stella is in the water, standing on the bottom rung. She climbs out of the water and continues up to rung 9.
Write an addition for this.

3. Andy is standing on rung 5. This subtraction shows what he does next.

$$5 - 7 = ?$$

Copy the subtraction and fill in the missing number to find which rung Andy is standing on now.

4. Debbie throws a ball from the top of the diving board and Arun catches it on the surface of the water.
Write a subtraction to show what happens to the ball.

This is a press-button control panel in the lift in a block of flats. Use it to answer Questions 5 to 9.

```
                                    10
                                    9
                                    8
                                    7
```

5. What number could be written on the ground-floor button?

```
                                    6
                                    5
                                    4
                                    3
```

6. Write a subtraction for a trip in the lift from the seventh floor down to the basement.

```
                                    2
                                    1
                    Ground
                    Floor        [  ]
                    Garage       -1
```

7. Angela uses the lift for a journey described by this addition.

$$-1 + 4 = \boxed{}$$

```
                    Basement     -2
                    Boiler
                    Room         -3
```

Complete the addition and describe her journey in words.

8. Adam took the lift from the boiler room and got out at the ninth floor.
How many floors has he risen by?

9. John was on the fifth floor. He got into the lift and pressed the button to go up three floors. When the lift stopped he did not get out but decided to go down to the basement.
How many floors did he descend?

10. Lisa entered the lift at the eighth floor, intending to go to the fourth floor, but she pressed a button which took her to the wrong floor. She then went up another six floors to get to the right floor.
a) Which button did she press first?
b) Copy and fill in the missing number and the missing plus or minus signs.

$$8 \bigcirc \boxed{} \bigcirc 6 = 4$$

11. A potholer measures his position below ground level using negative numbers. He climbs 20 m down the vertical shaft and then explores the 12 m long horizontal tunnel. At the end of it he finds a rope ladder and climbs up it for 4 m.

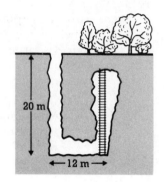

What is his position below ground level

a) when he is at the foot of the shaft
b) at the end of the tunnel
c) after climbing the rope ladder?

12 PERCENTAGES

FINDING PERCENTAGES

In Book 1B we saw that

$25\% = \frac{25}{100} = \frac{1}{4}$ and $50\% = \frac{50}{100} = \frac{1}{2}$ and $75\% = \frac{75}{100} = \frac{3}{4}$

EXERCISE 12a Complete each sentence.

1. £4 out of £8 is _____ %

2. 7 minutes out of 28 minutes is _____%

3. 20 children out of 40 children is _____ %

4. 2 days out of 8 days is _____ %

5. £15 out of £20 is _____ %

6. 3 miles out of 12 miles is _____%

7. 9 miles out of 12 miles is _____%

8. 32 pages out of 64 pages is _____%

9. 60 pence out of 80 pence is _____ %

10. 1500 people out of 2000 people is _____ %

119

FINDING PERCENTAGES OF QUANTITIES

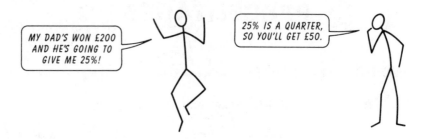

EXERCISE 12b

The book John is reading has 48 pages. He has read 75% of the pages.

a) How many pages has he read?

b) What percentage of the pages has John not yet read?

a) $75\% = \frac{3}{4}$

So 75% of $48 = \frac{3}{4}$ of 48

$= 36$

John has read 36 pages.

b) The percentage of the pages which John has not yet read

is $(100\% - 75\%) = 25\%$

1. The first-year pupils raised £44 for charity. They gave 75% of it to the Save the Children Fund.
   How much is that?

2. Andrew has 8 ballpens but only 2 of them work.
   a) What percentage of Andrew's pens work?
   b) What percentage of his pens do not work?

3. Pam took all the shots on her 24-exposure film and 18 of the pictures were good ones.

a) What fraction of the shots were good?

b) What percentage of the film gave good pictures?

4. Hotshot Juniors scored 36 goals last season. Minar Ali scored 9 of the goals.

a) What percentage of the goals did Minar score?

b) What percentage of the goals were scored by other players?

5. Mrs Reed bought 3 kg of new potatoes and 9 kg of baking potatoes.

What percentage of the whole bag of potatoes were

a) new ones   b) baking potatoes?

The distance by road from Bricktown to Stoneville is 32 miles. Kerry, Colin and Barry all started cycling from Bricktown towards Stoneville. Kerry cycled 16 miles and then gave up. Colin managed to go 24 miles before he stopped but Barry went the whole way to Stoneville.

6. What percentage of the total distance did Kerry cycle?

7. What percentage of the total distance was covered by Colin?

8. What percentage of the total distance did Barry go?

A market gardener planted 48 cabbage plants. A sharp frost killed 12 of them, and 24 were eaten by caterpillars. The rest grew well and were harvested.

9. What percentage of the plants were killed by frost?

10. What percentage of the plants were killed by caterpillars?

11. What percentage were harvested?

EXPRESSING A PERCENTAGE AS A DECIMAL

It is easy to find 25%, 50% or 75% of a quantity because they are all simple fractions. For other percentages however, we usually need a calculator and then it is more useful to express the percentage as a decimal,

e.g. $$35\% = \frac{35}{100} = 0{\cdot}35$$

EXERCISE 12c

Express 40% as a decimal.

$$40\% = \frac{40}{100} = 0{\cdot}4$$

Express each percentage as a decimal.

1.	70%	**3.**	20%	**5.**	90%	**7.**	60%
2.	10%	**4.**	80%	**6.**	30%	**8.**	50%

Express 53% as a decimal.

$$53\% = \frac{53}{100} = 0{\cdot}53$$

Express each percentage as a decimal.

9.	87%	**11.**	14%	**13.**	56%	**15.**	77%
10.	51%	**12.**	49%	**14.**	97%	**16.**	28%
17.	11%	**19.**	21%	**21.**	63%	**23.**	91%
18.	99%	**20.**	35%	**22.**	82%	**24.**	19%

Express 6% as a decimal.

$$6\% = \frac{6}{100} = 0\cdot06$$

Express each percentage as a decimal.

25. 9%   **26.** 2%   **27.** 5%   **28.** 1%

Express 125% as a decimal

$$125\% = \frac{125}{100} = 1\cdot25$$

A PERCENTAGE BIGGER THAN 100% GIVES A DECIMAL BIGGER THAN 1.

Express each percentage as a decimal.

29. 140%   **31.** 193%   **33.** 88%   **35.** 101%

30. 36%   **32.** 152%   **34.** 250%   **36.** 200%

MORE PERCENTAGES OF QUANTITIES

WHAT IS 80% OF 10 HOURS?

$$80\% = \frac{80}{100} = 0\cdot8$$

So 80% of 10 hours $= 0\cdot8 \times 10$

$= 8$ hours

"OF" MEANS "×"

EXERCISE 12d

Mary set out on a 15 mile trek but she completed only 60% of the course. How many miles did Mary cover?

$$60\% = \frac{60}{100} = 0{\cdot}6$$

So 60% of 15 miles $= 0{\cdot}6 \times 15$ miles

$$= 9 \text{ miles}$$

Find

1. 70% of £50
2. 90% of £20
3. 30% of 10 hours
4. 40% of 15 m
5. 20% of 30 days

6. 80% of 25 cm
7. 10% of 60 p
8. 60% of 20 minutes
9. 100% of 3 weeks
10. 90% of 270 pupils

Find   17% of £30

$$17\% = \frac{17}{100} = 0{\cdot}17$$

So   17% of £30 $= 0{\cdot}17 \times £30$

$$= £5.10$$

Find

11. 12% of 50 kilometres
12. 54% of 15 kilograms
13. 35% of 120 centimetres
14. 81% of £20
15. 11% of 10 years

16. 18% of 2 litres
17. 72% of 40 minutes
18. 26% of 10 kilometres
19. 44% of 50 seconds
20. 8% of 10 days

21. 70% of the 40 houses in one street have telephones.
How many houses have a telephone?

22. In the fourth year 55% of the 280 pupils play a musical instrument.
How many pupils is this?

23. In a geography test Govind got 72%. The test was marked out of 75.
How many marks did Govind get?

24. There were 240 teenagers at a disco and 65% of them were girls.
a) How many girls were at the disco?
b) What percentage of the teenagers were boys?

25. 15% of a box of 40 lettuces went bad and had to be thrown away.
How many lettuces went bad?

26. In a packet of mixed toffees, 36% are mint flavoured. There are 25 toffees in the bag.
a) What percentage of the toffees are not mint flavoured?
b) How many mint-flavoured toffees are there?

MIXED EXERCISE

EXERCISE 12e Find

1. 50% of £12

2. 25% of 28 days

3. 46% of £50

4. 25% of 4 hours

5. 10% of £3

6. 82% of 250 boys

7. 75% of 20 minutes

8. 20% of 10 months

9. 120% of £8

10. 200% of £7

Copy and complete each sentence.

11. 20 p is ____ % of 40 p.

12. £15 is ____ % of £20.

13. 3 days is ____ % of 4 days.

14. 10 minutes is ____ % of 40 minutes.

15. William earned £5 by cleaning cars. He spent 50% of it. How much did he spend?

16. On Tuesday evening after a meal, Tracy started by doing maths homework for half an hour. Then she went out with her friends for one hour before watching a half-hour programme on television. After that she went straight to bed.

What percentage of her time after the meal on Tuesday evening did Tracy spend

a) doing maths homework
b) with her friends
c) watching television?

1︎3 STATISTICS

FINDING THE MEAN

MY AVERAGE MARK IS 8. WHAT'S YOURS?

I'LL WORK IT OUT. I KNOW MY MARKS.

Frank got these marks for five tests: 7, 8, 6, 9, 4.

He worked out his average mark by adding up his separate marks, i.e. $7 + 8 + 6 + 9 + 5$. This came to 35.

He then divided this sum by 5 because there were five marks:
$$35 \div 5 = 7.$$

His answer, 7, is his average mark. (This means that if he had the same mark in all subjects, that mark would be 7.)

This way of averaging a set of numbers is called *finding the mean*. The answer is called the *mean*.

$$\text{Mean} = \frac{\text{Total amount}}{\text{Number of items}}$$

EXERCISE 13a

> Anna gets £1 pocket money each week, Peter gets £3 a week and Kalia gets £2 each week. Find the mean (average) amount of pocket money per week.
>
> $$\text{Total amount} = £1 + £3 + £2$$
> $$= £6$$
> $$\text{Mean amount} = £6 \div 3 = £2$$

1. Six pupils got the following marks on a test:

$$5, \ 7, \ 8, \ 4, \ 8, \ 4$$

What is the mean mark?

127

2. In three different shops, the price of a can of cola is 17 p, 15 p and 13 p.
What is the mean price?

3. Five people decided to pool their money. They put in the following amounts:

£10, £5, £6, £7 and £12

a) How much was in the pool?
b) If the five people had contributed equally to the total, how much would each have given?
c) What was the mean amount contributed to the pool?

4. The ages of the children in a swimming club are

9, 10, 8, 10, 11, 8, 12, 9, 12, 11, 10, 10

Find the mean age.

5. Find the mean of each set of numbers.
a) 2, 4, 8, 4, 7, 1, 7, 6, 5, 6
b) 12, 15, 13, 10, 24, 16
c) 24, 35, 44, 28, 34

6. Over a period of four hours, the number of buses that passed the school gate were counted. From this information it was found that the average number of buses was 3 each hour.
How many buses were counted?

The mean is not always a quantity that can exist.

Five children gave 2 p, 3 p, 2 p, 4 p and 5 p to a collection. Find the mean amount collected.

The total sum is 16 p
and the mean amount is 16 p ÷ 5 = 3·2 p

THIS MEANS THAT IF THE 16p COULD BE SHARED
EQUALLY AMONG THE CHILDREN, EACH WOULD GET 3·2p.

7. In four different shops the price of an HB pencil was 12 p, 14 p, 13 p and 15 p. Find the mean price.

8. Ten children got the following marks in a test:

8, 9, 7, 8, 5, 8, 6, 8, 4, 9

Find the mean mark.

9. In five different shops the price of a 200 g jar of instant coffee was

£2.80, £3.66, £2.95, £3.04, £2.99

Find the mean price of a jar of coffee.

10. A traffic survey found that the number of cars passing through a set of traffic lights averaged 65·8 cars each hour over a five hour period.
How many cars were counted?

FINDING THE RANGE

In the end of year tests,
Alice got these marks: 62, 54, 70, 68, 72.
Amjad got these marks: 49, 89, 57, 35, 67, 78.
They decided to compare their marks.

Alice worked out her average mark: it was 65·2.
Amjad worked out his average mark: it was 62·5.

The difference between Alice's highest and lowest mark was
72 − 54 = 18.
For Amjad's set of marks, this difference was   89 − 35 = 54.

> The difference between the highest and lowest number
> in a set is called the *range*.

EXERCISE 13b 1. The heights of five boys are 120 cm, 135 cm, 141 cm, 160 cm and 148 cm.
What is the range of these heights?

2. The prices of a particular ball-point pen in ten different shops were

27 p, 32 p, 18 p, 25 p, 25 p, 45 p, 19 p, 22 p, 19 p, 27 p

Find the range of these prices.

3. Find the range of each of the following sets of quantities.
a) 2 p, 14 p, 7 p, 10 p, 11 p
b) 9 mm, 5 mm, 12 mm, 4 mm, 2 mm
c) 1·5 ℓ, 1·1 ℓ, 1·2 ℓ, 1·4 ℓ
d) £4.20, £3.34, £1.03, 95 p

4. Ten 13-year-old boys measured their heights. They were

144 cm, 132 cm, 175 cm, 135 cm, 152 cm,
145 cm, 161 cm, 131 cm, 166 cm, 132 cm

Find a) the range of these heights   b) the mean height.

5. These are the marks for a maths test for a group of pupils.

10, 12, 3, 12, 15, 8, 9, 12, 14, 13,
5, 11, 12, 10, 11, 7, 9, 12, 13, 12

Find
a) the range of these marks
b) the mean mark.

6. A group of adults gave their loose change for a charity collection. They gave

12 p, 25 p, 15 p, 30 p, 15 p, 45 p,
10 p, 17 p, 25 p, 30 p, 58 p, 19 p

a) Find the range of the amounts given.
b) If each adult had been able to give an equal amount to get the same total, how much, to the nearest penny, would this have been?

GROUPING INFORMATION

These are the test marks for a group of pupils. The test was marked out of 15.

6	4	8	10	6	12	10
5	9	10	14	3	4	9
12	12	8	13	2	9	7
14	12	9	11	15	8	12

We know how to find the mean mark and how to find the range of the marks.

There are sixteen possible marks (0 to 15). Some of these do not appear in the list and others appear only once or twice.

A frequency table listing all the possible marks would not give us a helpful picture so we group the marks to make more sense of them. We have chosen four groups for this frequency table. (Remember to work down the columns, making a tally mark in the tally column next to the appropriate group.)

Mark	Tally	Frequency
0–3	II	2
4–7	₩ I	6
8–11	₩ ₩ I	11
12–15	₩ IIII	9
	Total	28

This bar chart illustrates the set of marks.

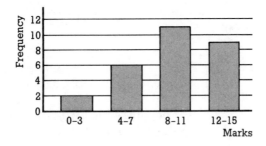

EXERCISE 13c **1.** For an English project, pupils were asked to investigate the number of letters per word from a paragraph of the book *Tom's Midnight Garden*. This is a list of the number of letters per word.

4	3	3	5	3	14	4	6	4	3	9
2	4	4	1	4	6	4	3	6	4	6
3	7	4	1	6	4	5	3	4	3	6
4	3	4	6	6	5	3	3	2	7	3
4	10	11								

a) How many words were there in this paragraph?

b) Copy and fill in this frequency table.

Number of letters	Tally	Frequency
1–3		
4–6		
7–9		
10–12		
More than 12		
Total		

c) Make a bar chart to illustrate the frequency table.

2. Investigate the number of letters per word on page 6 of this book. (Ignore any figures and notice that "first-year" counts as two words.)

a) Make a list of the numbers of letters per word.

b) Make a frequency table for this list using the groups

1–3 letters, 4–6 letters, 7–9 letters,
10–12 letters, more than 12 letters.

c) Illustrate your frequency table with a bar chart.

3. This frequency table is based on the journey times of the employees of Able Engineering Co.

Journey time in minutes	0–14	15–29	30–44	45–59
Number of employees	3	8	6	2

a) How many employees took part in this survey?

b) How many employees had a journey time of less than half an hour?

c) Is it possible to tell from the table how many had a journey time of five minutes?

4. A group of 10-year-olds were asked how much pocket money they were given each week. This frequency table was made from the information.

Weekly pocket money (pence)	0–49	50–99	100–149	150–199	200–249
Number of children	10	15	42	68	18

a) How many children were asked how much pocket money they received?
b) How many children got more than 99 p each week?
c) How many children got no pocket money?

5. Make your own survey of the pocket money given to your friends and class mates.

a) Start by preparing a frequency table like the one in Question 1, but use the groups of Question 4. You may have to add further groups, i.e. 250–299 p, and so on.
b) Ask between 30 and 50 children how much pocket money they get each week and put a tally mark in the appropriate column each time you are told an amount.
c) Illustrate your survey with a bar chart.

6. This bar chart illustrates a survey into the number of books (not school books) read each week by some 16-year-olds.

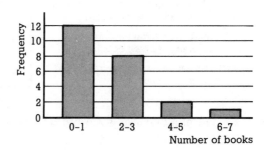

a) How many read less than two books each week?
b) How many read four or more books each week?
c) Why can you not tell how many read four books each week?

READING BAR CHARTS

Bar charts can be used for information other than frequencies. When you look at a bar chart, read the labels on the axes.

The bars are usually vertical but can be horizontal.

EXERCISE 13d 1. This bar chart gives rough guidelines on the distances that should be allowed between moving cars.

At 30 mph   3 car lengths

At 50 mph   5 car lengths

At 60 mph   6 car lengths

a) Roughly what distance should a car travelling at 70 mph keep from the car in front?
b) What rule has been used to decide the safe distance?
c) Write two sentences on why this rule is only a rough guide.

2. This bar chart shows the cost of fuel in an average home with central heating.

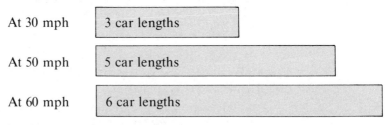

Appliances Cooking Hot water Central heating

Off-peak electric heating and hot water; electric cooking   A

Solid fuel central heating and hot water; electric cooking   B

Gas central heating and hot water; gas cooking   C

No numbers are given but we can get an idea about the relative costs.

a) Which is the most expensive method overall?
b) Which is the cheapest?
c) Which is the most expensive method of producing hot water?
d) Which is the cheapest method of cooking?
e) Which is the cheapest method of heating?

3. This bar chart shows the average monthly rainfall in Norwich.

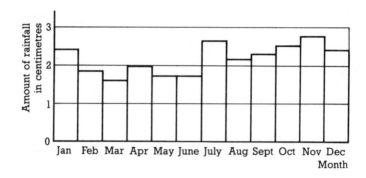

a) Which month is the wettest and which the driest?

b) Does more rain fall in the spring or in the autumn?

c) When would you recommend taking a holiday in Norwich and why?

d) How much rain falls in April in Norwich?

4. This is a bar chart showing the average daily hours of sunshine in Aberdeen and Margate.

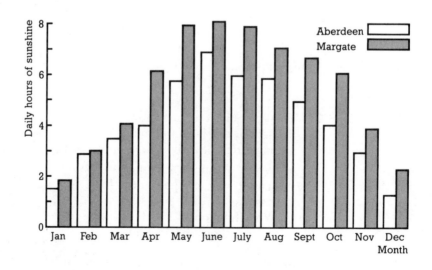

a) Is there more sunshine in Margate or in Aberdeen?

b) Which month is the finest in both towns?

c) Which month has the least sunshine in each town?

PIE CHARTS

YOU CUT, I'LL CHOOSE.

Pie charts are used to show how something is shared out.

EXERCISE 13e **1.** Here is a *pie*. Draw a bigger one in your book. Alan gets half the pie and Matt and Jen get a quarter each.
Draw lines on your "pie" to show each person's share. Label each slice with its owners name.

Diagrams like the one that you have drawn are called pie charts.

2. This pie chart shows how the school day is shared out among different activities.

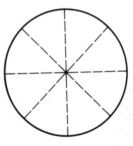

a) What fraction of the school day is spent on lessons?

b) What fraction of the day is spent on meals and breaks?

c) If the school days lasts from 9 a.m. to 3 p.m., how many minutes are taken up with meals and breaks?

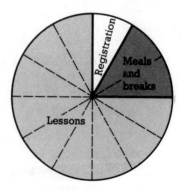

3. This pie chart shows the proportions of different coloured sweets in a tube of smarties.

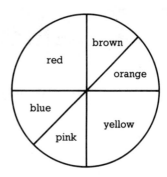

a) What fraction of the sweets are red?

b) What fraction of the sweets are blue?

c) If the tube contained 80 sweets, how many yellow ones are there?

4. This pie chart shows the proportions of various nutrients in a packet of cornflakes.

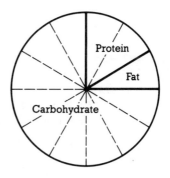

a) What fraction of the nutrients is fat?

b) How many grams of fat are there in a serving of 48 g?

c) How many grams of protein are there in a serving of 48 g?

5. A tin contains 40 mixed biscuits. There are 10 chocolate biscuits, 5 cream biscuits, 15 iced biscuits and the rest are plain.

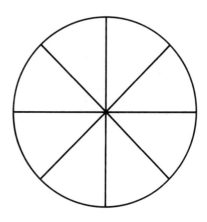

a) What fraction of the biscuits are chocolate?

b) What fraction are cream biscuits?

c) What fraction are plain?

d) Trace this pie chart and use it to show the fraction of each type of biscuit in the tin. Don't forget to label each slice of the pie.

14 PERIMETER AND AREA

The distance all round a shape is called its perimeter.

1 cm ▢ This square is called a centimetre square.
Its area is 1 square centimetre.

1 square centimetre is written as 1 cm².

2 cm ┆ 3 cm

We can find the area of this rectangle by counting the number of 1 centimetre squares needed to fill it. We can also see that this number is given if we multiply the length by the breadth.

Area of a rectangle = Length × Breadth

EXERCISE 14a

Find the perimeter and area of this table top.

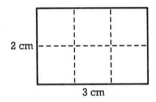

TO FIND THE PERIMETER, MARK A STARTING POINT, THEN WRITE DOWN THE LENGTHS OF ALL THE SIDES IN ORDER, UNTIL YOU GET BACK TO THE STARTING POINT.

TO FIND THE AREA, I MUST MULTIPLY THE LENGTH BY THE BREADTH.

120 cm
80 cm
80 cm
120 cm

Perimeter = 120 + 80 + 120 + 80 cm

= 400 cm

Area = Length × Breadth

"BREADTH" IS ANOTHER WORD FOR "WIDTH".

= 120 × 80 cm²

= 9600 cm²

For each shape find
a) its perimeter,   b) its area.

1.

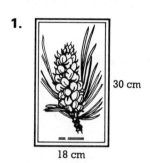

30 cm

18 cm

2.

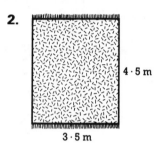

4·5 m

3·5 m

3.

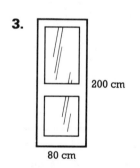

200 cm

80 cm

4.

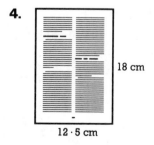

18 cm

12·5 cm

5.

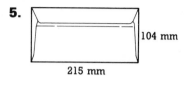

104 mm

215 mm

6.

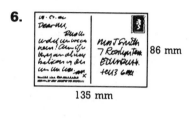

86 mm

135 mm

7.

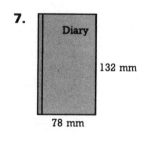

Diary

132 mm

78 mm

8.

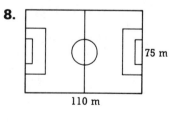

75 m

110 m

9.   A paving slab measuring 40 cm by 40 cm.

10.   A table mat measuring 24 cm by 15 cm.

COMPOUND SHAPES

We can often find the area of a compound shape by dividing it into two or more rectangles.

EXERCISE 14b

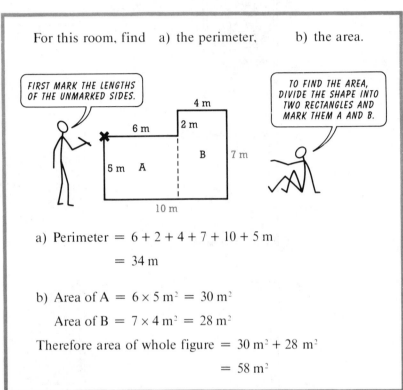

For this room, find   a) the perimeter,   b) the area.

FIRST MARK THE LENGTHS OF THE UNMARKED SIDES.

TO FIND THE AREA, DIVIDE THE SHAPE INTO TWO RECTANGLES AND MARK THEM A AND B.

a) Perimeter = 6 + 2 + 4 + 7 + 10 + 5 m

        = 34 m

b) Area of A = 6 × 5 m² = 30 m²

    Area of B = 7 × 4 m² = 28 m²

Therefore area of whole figure = 30 m² + 28 m²

                    = 58 m²

For each question, first sketch the diagram. Find

a) the perimeter,   b) the area.

Do not forget to put in the unmarked lengths first and then divide each shape into two or more rectangles.

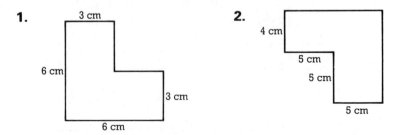

3.

6 mm

20 mm

12 mm

4 mm

7.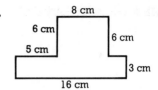

8 cm

6 cm

6 cm

5 cm

3 cm

16 cm

4.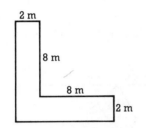

2 m

8 m

8 m

2 m

8.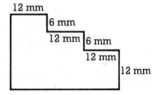

12 mm

6 mm

12 mm 6 mm

12 mm

12 mm

5.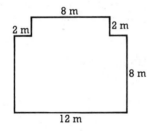

8 m

2 m

2 m

8 m

12 m

9.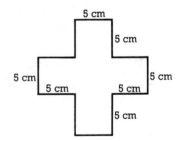

5 cm

5 cm

5 cm

5 cm

5 cm

5 cm

5 cm

5 cm

6.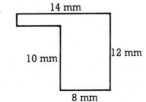

14 mm

10 mm

12 mm

8 mm

10.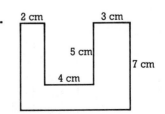

2 cm

3 cm

5 cm

7 cm

4 cm

AREA OF A TRIANGLE

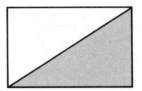

A diagonal of a rectangle divides the rectangle into two identical pieces.

Therefore the area of the shaded triangle is one half of the area of the rectangle.

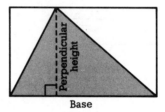

If we draw a triangle in a rectangle we see that the area of the triangle is half the area of the rectangle.

Since the area of the rectangle is found by multiplying the length by the breadth we get

THIS IS THE LENGTH OF THE RECTANGLE.

Area of triangle = $\frac{1}{2}$(base × perpendicular height)

THIS IS THE BREADTH OF THE RECTANGLE.

Notice that the perpendicular height is always at right angles to the base. The base of a triangle is any side from which we take the perpendicular height.

EXERCISE 14c

For each triangle, state the length of
a) the base   b) the perpendicular height.

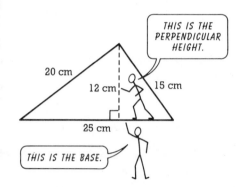

a) The length of the base
   is 25 cm.

b) The perpendicular height
   is 12 cm.

a) The length of the base
   is 5 cm.

b) The perpendicular height
   is 10 cm.

For each triangle write down the length of
a) the base,   b) the perpendicular height.

1.

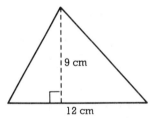

9 cm

12 cm

3.

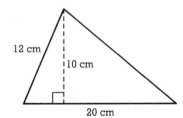

12 cm

10 cm

20 cm

2.

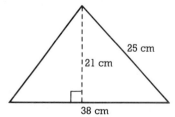

25 cm

21 cm

38 cm

4.

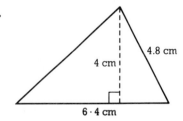

4.8 cm

4 cm

6·4 cm

5.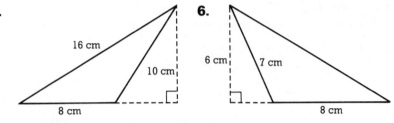

6.

Sometimes you will need to turn the page round to look at the triangle from a different direction.

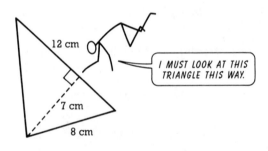

For this triangle, give the length of
a) the base   b) the perpendicular height.

I MUST LOOK AT THIS TRIANGLE THIS WAY.

a) The length of the base is 12 cm.

b) The perpendicular height is 7 cm.

For each triangle find the length of
a) the base   b) the perpendicular height.

7.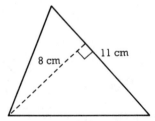

8.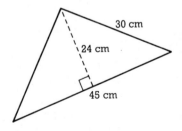

EXERCISE 14d

What is the area of this triangle ?

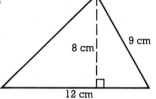

$$\text{Area} = \tfrac{1}{2}(\text{base} \times \text{height})$$
$$= \tfrac{1}{2} \times (12 \times 8) \text{ cm}^2$$
$$= \tfrac{1}{2} \times 96 \text{ cm}^2$$
$$= 48 \text{ cm}^2$$

Find the areas of the following triangles.

1.

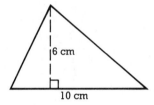

4.

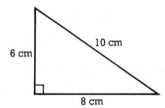

2.

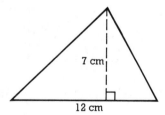

5.

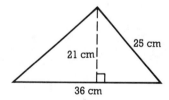

3.

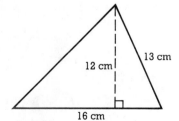

6.

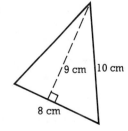

7.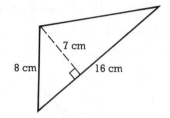

9.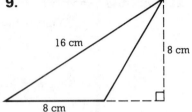

8.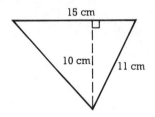

10.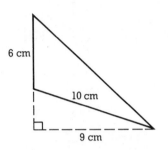

COMPOUND SHAPES

Sometimes a shape is made up from a mixture of rectangles and triangles.

EXERCISE 14e

What is the area of the side of this house?

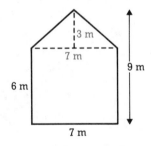

DIVIDE THE SHAPE INTO A RECTANGLE AND A TRIANGLE, AND REMEMBER TO PUT IN THE UNMARKED LENGTHS.

Area of rectangle $= 7 \times 6 \text{ m}^2 = 42 \text{ m}^2$

Area of triangle $= \frac{1}{2} \times 7 \times 3 \text{ m}^2$

$= \frac{1}{2} \times 21 \text{ m}^2$

$= 10\frac{1}{2} \text{ m}^2$

Therefore area of side of house $= 42 + 10\frac{1}{2} \text{ m}^2$

$= 52\frac{1}{2} \text{ m}^2$

In each question from 1 to 6, sketch the diagram and find the area of the shape.

1.

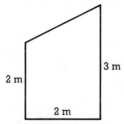

The side of a 'lean-to' shed.

5.

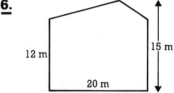

A plot of ground.

2.

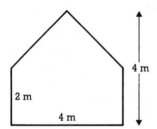

The end wall of a garage.

6.

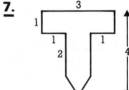

The end wall of a factory building.

3.

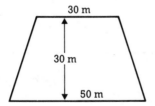

The section through a dam wall.

7.

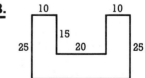

The section through a spinning top. (All measurements are in cm.)

4.

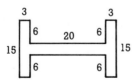

The cross-section of a metal bar. (All measurements are in mm.)

8.

The cross-section of a water-trough. (All measurements are in cm.)

In Questions 9 to 12, using 1 cm dotted paper, copy the diagram and measure the lengths you need to find the area (in square centimetres) of each shape. Then find the area.

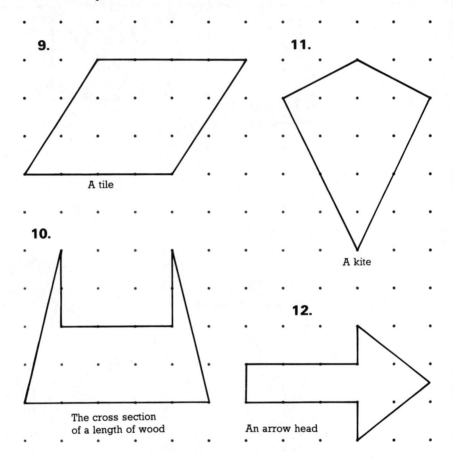

9.

A tile

11.

A kite

10.

The cross section of a length of wood

12.

An arrow head

15 COORDINATES

We saw in Book 1B that points can be located on a grid by starting from a point O, drawing an *x*-axis across the grid and a *y*-axis up the grid.

A is 3 units *across* from O and 2 units *up* from O. The coordinates of A are $(3, 2)$.

We always put the *x*-coordinate first. It is the distance across.

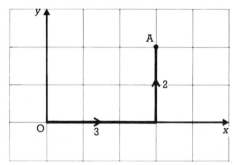

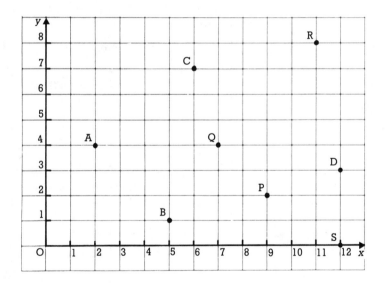

Write down the coordinates of

1. A   **2.** B   **3.** C   **4.** D

Write down

5. the *x*-coordinate of P   **7.** the *x*-coordinate of Q

6. the *y*-coordinate of R   **8.** the *y*-coordinate of S.

NEGATIVE COORDINATES

If A(1, 7), B(4, 4) and C(1, 1) are three corners of a square, we can see that the fourth corner, D, is two squares to the left of the *y*-axis.

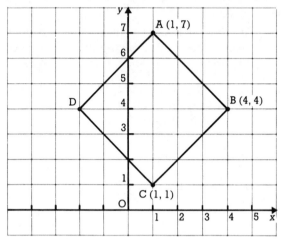

To describe the position of D we must extend the scale on the *x*-axis to the left of zero.

We do this by using *negative numbers*, −1, −2, −3 . . .

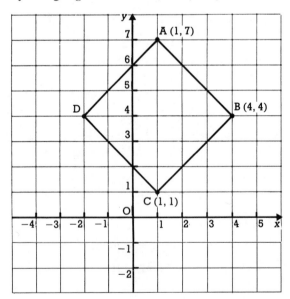

Now we can see that D is the point (−2, 4).

We can extend the scale on the *y*-axis in the same way using negative numbers below the origin.

EXERCISE 15b Use this diagram for Questions 1 and 2.

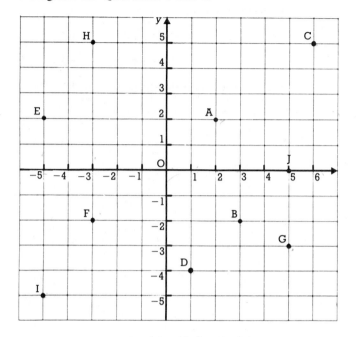

1. Write down the *x*-coordinate of each of the points A, B, C, D, E, F, G, H, I, J and O (the origin).

2. Write down the *y*-coordinate of each of the points A, B, C, D, E, H, I and J.

A point Q has a *y*-coordinate of -10. How many squares above or below the *x*-axis is the point Q?

Q is 10 squares below the *x*-axis.

How many squares above or below the *x*-axis is each of the following points?

3. P: the *y*-coordinate is -5 6. B: the *y*-coordinate is 10

4. L: the *y*-coordinate is $+3$ 7. A: the *y*-coordinate is 0

5. M: the *y*-coordinate is -1 8. D: the *y*-coordinate is -4

How many squares to the left or to the right of the y-axis is each of the following points?

9. Q: the x-coordinate is 3

12. S: the x-coordinate is -7

10. R: the x-coordinate is -5

13. V: the x-coordinate is 0

11. T: the x-coordinate is $+2$

14. G: the x-coordinate is -9

Write down the coordinates of the point A.

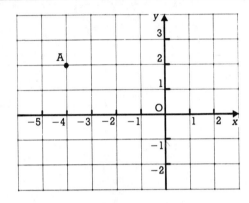

A is the point $(-4, 2)$.

15. Write down the coordinates of the points A, B, C, D, E, F, G, H, I and J.

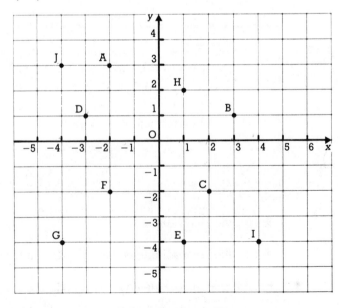

In Questions 16 to 18 draw your own set of axes and scale each one from -5 to 5.

16. Mark the points: $A(-3, 4)$, $B(-1, 4)$, $C(1, 3)$, $D(1, 2)$, $E(-1, 1)$, $F(1, 0)$, $G(1, -1)$, $H(-1, -2)$, $I(-3, -2)$.
Join the points in alphabetical order and join I to A.

17. Mark the points: $A(4, -1)$, $B(4, 2)$, $C(3, 3)$, $D(2, 3)$, $E(2, 4)$, $F(1, 4)$, $G(1, 3)$, $H(-2, 3)$, $I(-3, 2)$, $J(-3, -1)$.
Join the points in alphabetical order and join J to A.

18. Mark the points: $A(2, 1)$, $B(-1, 3)$, $C(-3, 0)$, $D(0, -2)$.
Join the points to make the figure ABCD. What is the name of the figure?

EXERCISE 15c Draw your own set of axes for each question in this exercise. Mark a scale on each axis from -10 to $+10$.

In Questions 1 to 10 mark the points A and B and then find the length of the line AB.

1. $A(2, 2)$, $B(-4, 2)$ **6.** $A(5, -1)$, $B(5, 6)$

2. $A(-2, -1)$, $B(6, -1)$ **7.** $A(-2, 4)$, $B(-7, 4)$

3. $A(-4, -4)$, $B(-4, 2)$ **8.** $A(-1, -2)$, $B(-8, -2)$

4. $A(1, -6)$, $B(1, -8)$ **9.** $A(-3, 5)$, $B(-3, -6)$

5. $A(3, 2)$, $B(5, 2)$ **10.** $A(-2, -4)$, $B(-2, 7)$

In Questions 11 to 15, the points A, B and C are three corners of a square ABCD. Mark the points and find the point D. Give the coordinates of D.

11. $A(1, 1)$, $B(1, -1)$, $C(-1, -1)$

12. $A(1, 3)$, $B(6, 3)$, $C(6, -2)$

13. $A(3, 3)$, $B(3, -1)$, $C(-1, -1)$

14. $A(-2, -1)$, $B(-2, 3)$, $C(-6, 3)$

15. $A(-5, -3)$, $B(-1, -3)$, $C(-1, 1)$

In Questions 16 to 21, mark the points A and B and the point C, the midpoint of the line AB. Give the coordinates of C.

16. $A(2, 2)$, $B(6, 2)$ **19.** $A(2, 4)$, $B(6, 2)$

17. $A(2, 3)$, $B(2, -5)$ **20.** $A(2, 1)$, $B(-4, 5)$

18. $A(-1, 3)$, $B(-7, 3)$ **21.** $A(-7, -3)$, $B(5, 3)$

16 USING ARITHMETIC

WORKING OUT THE COST OF POSTAGE

This is a list of postal charges (July 1990) for letters within the United Kingdom.

Letter Post

Weight not over	First Class	Second Class	Weight not over	First Class	Second Class
60 g	20 p	15 p	500 g	£1.02	78 p
100 g	30 p	24 p	600 g	£1.25	95 p
150 g	37 p	28 p	700 g	£1.45	£1.10
200 g	45 p	34 p	750 g	£1.55	£1.15
250 g	54 p	42 p	800 g	£1.65	Not admissible over 750 g
300 g	62 p	49 p	900 g	£1.80	
350 g	71 p	56 p	1000 g	£1.95	
400 g	80 p	63 p	Each extra 250 g or part thereof 50 p		
450 g	90 p	70 p			

EXERCISE 16a

Find the cost of posting 2 letters, each weighing 50 g, and one letter weighing 220 g; all to be sent first class.

THE 50g LETTERS ARE NOT OVER 60g – SO THEY COST 20p.

THE 220g LETTER IS OVER 200g, BUT IT IS NOT OVER 250g SO IT COSTS 54p.

The cost is $2 \times 20\,p + 54\,p$

$= 94\,p$

Find the cost of posting

1. 4 letters, all under 60 g, by first-class post

2. 5 letters, all under 60 g, by second-class post

3. 3 letters by first-class post, two of which weigh 50 g and one weighs 140 g

4. 4 letters, each weighing 90 g, by second-class post

5. 2 letters, each weighing 80 g, and 3 letters, each weighing 120 g, all by first-class post.

PAYING FOR THE PHOTOCOPIER

Grange School rents its photocopier.

The school has to pay rent each quarter (i.e. every three months) and 1 p for each copy made.

EXERCISE 16b

> 8500 photocopies were made in the first quarter of 1990, and the rent for that quarter was £350. What was the bill for that quarter?
>
> The charge for 8500 copies is 8500×1 p $= 8500$ p
>
> $= £85$
>
> The rent is $= £350$
>
> The bill for 'rent' plus 'charge for copies' $= £350 + £85$
>
> $= £435$

Find the bill for the quarter when

1. the rent is £200 and 2500 copies are made

2. the rent is £330 and 9000 copies are made

3. the rent is £425 and 10 000 copies are made

4. the rent is £250 and 20 000 copies are made.

Hill School also rents a photocopier. The rent is £200 for each quarter in 1990. The cost of each copy is 1 p. Find the bill for each quarter when

5. 7800 copies are made in the first quarter

6. 10 250 copies are made in the second quarter

7. 12 500 copies are made in the third quarter

8. 19 650 copies are made in the last quarter.

9. How much does Hill School have to pay for photocopying for the whole year?

10. The governors at Hill School decide to buy a photocopier. This costs them £6000. Paper costs £2 for 500 sheets. They make 50 000 copies each year.
a) How much does the paper cost for one year?
b) If the photocopier lasts 5 years, what is the total cost for 5 years of the photocopier and paper?
c) How much does this work out for each year?

HOLIDAYS

The cost of a holiday depends on where it is, when it is, how long it is, the type of travel, and so on. Holiday brochures need to be read very carefully to find all the charges for a holiday.

EXERCISE 16c This is part of a brochure offering self-catering flats in France. The prices given are for one week's rent in £s per flat.

	MAY	JUNE	JULY	AUGUST	SEPTEMBER
FLAT A (sleeps 2)	90	120	120	200	100
FLAT B (sleeps 3)	100	140	140	230	110
FLAT C (sleeps 3) large terrace	120	160	160	270	140
FLAT D (sleeps 4) large terrace	150	200	200	300	170

Find out how much it costs to rent

1. Flat A for two weeks in August.

2. Flat B for three weeks in July.

3. Flat C for the last week in August and the first week in September.

4. Flat A for the last two weeks in July and the first in August.

5. Flat D for the last week in May and the first week in June.

6. Flat C for the last week in June and the first two weeks in July.

When a flat is booked, the travel agent asks for a deposit of 10% of the total rent.

Find the deposit to be paid on Flat A booked for two weeks in July.

The rent is 2 × £120   = £240
The deposit is 10% of £240 = £(0·10 × 240)
                             = £24

Find the deposit needed for booking

7. Flat C for two weeks in September

8. Flat D for one week in August

9. Flat B for three weeks in May

10. Flat A for the last week in July and the first two weeks in August.

ADAPTING RECIPES

This recipe is enough for 4 people.

> **CRUNCHY CHICKEN**
>
> 4 chicken legs
> 50 g salted crisps
> 25 g butter
>
> Crush the crisps with a rolling pin. Melt the butter. Coat each chicken piece with butter and then roll in the crushed crisps. Place in an oven-proof dish and bake for about 40 minutes at 200 °C.

EXERCISE 16d Use the recipe for crunchy chicken for Questions 1 to 3.

1. Write out the list of ingredients needed for two people.

2. Write out the list of ingredients needed for six people.

3. Mrs. Leal uses this recipe for a party and makes enough for 10 people.
   a) How many chicken legs should she buy?
   b) Crisps are sold in 50 g bags. How many bags will she need?
   c) This quantity fits into the oven. How long will it take to cook?

4. The recipe below makes a cake big enough for eight portions.

> **FRUIT CAKE**
>
> | | |
> |---|---|
> | 100 g margarine | 200 g mixed dried fruit |
> | 100 g soft brown sugar | 50 g candied cherries |
> | 2 eggs | 50 g mixed peel |
> | 150 g self-raising flour | 20 ml milk |
>
> Cream the butter and sugar. Beat in the eggs with a little flour. Mix in the rest of the flour and the milk. Stir in the remaining ingredients. Cook in a 20 cm diameter tin in a slow oven for about one hour.

   a) Write down the list of ingredients needed to make a cake twice as big. How many portions will you get from a cake this size?
   b) Write down the ingredients needed to make a cake half the size. How many portions will you get from a cake this size?
   c) Mr Arnold uses this recipe to make a cake big enough for 20 portions. Write down the list of the ingredients that he uses.

KEEPING THE SCORE

EXERCISE 16e These are the rules for one version of the game of pool:

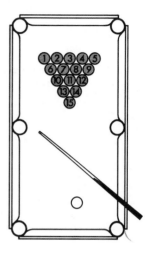

The cue ball must knock a numbered ball into a pocket, this is called potting a ball.

The player must say which ball he is trying to pot. The score is the number on the ball that has been potted.

A player continues his turn until he fails to pot the ball or misses it.

If a player misses, the other player gets the score for that ball.

When all the balls have been potted, the player with the highest score wins.

1. Ian pots the following balls: ② ④ ⑫ and then doesn't pot the next ball. What is his score?

2. Merle pots these balls, ⑤ ⑨ ⑩ and then calls the 11 but misses it. What is her score and what score does she give her opponent?

3. James and Andrea have a game. Andrea plays first. Each ball shown is a pot. Copy and complete the score board on the next page for this game.

Andrea: ⑩ ②

James: ③ ⑦ ⑫ calls 8 but misses

Andrea: ① ④

James: ⑥ calls 15 but misses

Andrea: ⑮ ⑨ calls 8 but misses

James: (11) (5) (8) calls 14 but misses

Andrea: no pot

James: (14)

Andrea: (13)

A	J
1̶2̶	22
20	

4. Who wins?

EXERCISE 16f In a game of darts, numbers on the edge of the board show the score for that section.

However, the outer dark ring scores double, the middle dark ring scores treble, the small circle in the middle scores 50 and the ring just outside it scores 25.

1. Find the score on each of these boards.

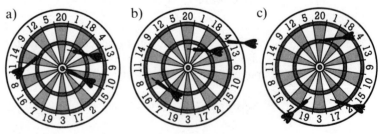

a)   b)   c)

This is one version of the rules:
Each player starts with a score of 301.

For each turn, three darts are thrown and the score is subtracted from the total. A player must start with a double and end with a double. The first player to reach 0 wins, but he must not score more than he needs.

> On Peter's first go he scores double 20, treble 1, miss.
> What is his score on the board after this go?
>
> Score from the darts is $(2 \times 20) + (3 \times 1) + 0$
>
> $\qquad\qquad\qquad\qquad\qquad = 43$
>
> Score on the board is $301 - 43 = 258$

2. Adele and Gwen play a game of darts. Copy and complete the board after each turn.

A	G
~~301~~ 272	301

a) Adele's first turn: miss, double 5, 19.
b) Gwen's first turn: double 5, 20, 1.
c) Adele's second turn: 20, treble 10, miss.
d) Gwen's second turn: 50, double 4, 7.
e) Adele's third turn: 19, 7, 5.
f) Gwen's third turn: miss, 5, 50.
g) Adele's fourth turn: double 20, treble 20, 1.
h) Gwen's fourth turn: treble 19, miss, treble 1.
i) Can either of them finish on their next turn?

17 PROBABILITY

EQUALLY LIKELY EVENTS

If a coin is tossed, it can land heads up or tails up. If the coin is a fair one, these two events are equally likely.

EXERCISE 17a **1.** If a dice is tossed, what are the possible scores that you can get? Are all these scores equally likely?

2. If Rebecca decides to pick out one card from an ordinary pack of playing cards, how many possible choices does she have? Is each of these possibilities equally likely?

3. A bag contains one red disc and one blue disc. Are the chances of taking out a red disc the same as the chances of taking out a blue one?

4. If the bag contained two red discs and one blue disc, would the chances of taking out a red disc or of a blue disc be the same?

162

PROBABILITY

WHAT ARE THE ODDS THAT I WILL THROW A SIX?

If you throw an ordinary dice fairly, it is reasonable to assume that you are as likely to throw a six as any other number from one to six.

Throwing a six is only 1 of 6 equally likely events, so the chance of throwing a six is 1 out of 6, or $\frac{1}{6}$.

Expressing the chance as a fraction gives a way of measuring that chance.

Probability is the word used for the measure of chance.

Therefore the probability that you will throw a 6 is $\frac{1}{6}$.

EXERCISE 17b In this exercise, assume that all the possible outcomes are equally likely.

1. What is the probability of throwing a 2 with a dice?

2. A box contains ten different coloured pencils including one red one.
If one pencil is taken, what is the probability that it is the red pencil?

3. What is the probability of choosing the letter A from the letters in the word SALE?

4. What is the probability of throwing a 3 with a dice?

5. What is the probability of choosing a prime number from the numbers

6, 7, 8, 9, 10?

6. In a raffle, 200 tickets are sold. If you bought one ticket, what is the probability that you will win first prize?

7. One card is drawn from a pack of 52 ordinary playing cards. What is the probability that it is the ace of hearts?

8. What is the probability of choosing a number that is exactly divisible by 5 from the numbers

    6, 7, 8, 9, 10, 11, 12?

9. What is the probability of choosing a multiple of 3 from the numbers

    4, 5, 6, 7, 8?

10. A number is chosen from the whole numbers from 20 to 30 inclusive. What is the probability that it is a prime number?

EVENTS THAT CAN HAPPEN MORE THAN ONCE

This bag contains 5 black discs and 8 white discs.

There are 5 equally likely ways of picking a black disc.

There are 13 equally likely ways of picking any disc.

Therefore 5 out of these 13 equally likely ways give a black disc. So the probability is $\frac{5}{13}$.

> The probability that an event happens is given by the fraction
>
> $$\frac{\text{number of ways that the event can happen}}{\text{total number of equally likely events}}$$

THIS MEANS THAT EACH LETTER IS
EQUALLY LIKELY TO BE CHOSEN.

EXERCISE 17c

One letter is chosen at random from the word DIFFICULT.
What is the probability that it is an I ?

There are nine letters in DIFFICULT so there are 9
equally likely choices, and 2 of these are I.

So the probability of choosing I is $\frac{2}{9}$.

1. A bag contains 4 white counters and 6 red counters. What is
the probability of taking out a white counter?

2. A number is chosen at random from the numbers

1, 2, 3, 4, 5, 6, 7, 8, 9, 10

What is the probability that it is an even number?

3. What is the probability of throwing *4 or higher* with a dice?

4. A lucky dip contains 50 boxes. Ten of these boxes contain a
prize, the rest are empty. What is the probability of picking out
a box that has a prize in it?

5. One card is drawn at random from an ordinary pack of 52
playing cards. Give the probability that it is
a) an ace   c) a red card
b) a heart   d) a picture card (include the aces).

6. One letter is chosen at random from the letters in the word
DIFFICULT.
What is the probability that it is
a) the letter F   c) a vowel
b) the letter D   d) a symmetrical letter?

CERTAINTY AND IMPOSSIBILITY ━━━━━━━━━━━━━━━━━━━━

EXERCISE 17d This bag contains five black discs.

1. What fraction of the discs in the bag are black?

2. What are the chances of taking a black disc from the bag?

3. What is the probability of taking a black disc from the bag?

4. What are the chances of removing a red disc from the bag? Write this as a probability.

If an event is certain to happen, the probability that it happens is 1. If an event is impossible, the probability that it happens is 0.

Most events fall somewhere between impossible and certain.

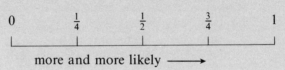

EXERCISE 17e 1. A bag holds 2 red counters, 3 blue counters and 1 yellow counter. 1 counter is drawn from the bag. What is the probability that it is

a) a red counter,
b) a yellow counter,
c) a black counter?

2. A dice is thrown. What is the probability of scoring

a) 1 or more,   b) 3 or more,   c) 7 or more?

3. A bag holds twenty tickets numbered 1 to 20. One ticket is drawn from the bag.
What is the probability that the number on it is

a) a multiple of 5   b) an even number?

4. A card is drawn from an ordinary pack of 52 playing cards. What is the probability that it is

a) a joker, c) a black card,

b) the two of clubs, d) a red or a black card?

5. One letter is chosen at random from the letters in the word MATHEMATICS. What is the probability that it is

a) the letter B, c) a vowel,

b) the letter T, d) a consonant?

USING STATISTICAL INFORMATION

To answer a question like this we need some information.

A survey carried out into the faults that developed in some makes of television sets gave the following results.

Model	Number that developed a fault in the first five years	Total number of sets in the survey	Practical probability	
			Fraction	Decimal
Cony	25	100		
Hitchi	5	50		
Thorson	60	120		
Elite	63	90		

EXERCISE 17f 1. To use the information in the table above, we have to compare the different makes. For each make find the number that developed a fault as a fraction of the total number of that make in the survey. This fraction gives the *practical probability*.

Copy the table and fill in the fraction column.

2. Fractions are easier to compare if they are expressed as decimals. Write each of your answers to Question 1 as a decimal, and then fill in the last column of the table.

3. What is the probability of a Cony television failing in the first five years?

4. If you decide to buy a Hitchi set, would you take out the extra five-year guarantee? Write one sentence giving reasons for your answer.

5. An Elite set is much cheaper than the other sets. Would you buy one of these sets? Write one sentence giving reasons for your answer.

6. Which of the four makes seems to be the most reliable?

7. This bar chart illustrates the results of a survey to test the water resistances of watches.

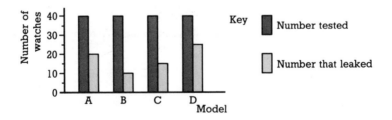

Each of these models claimed to be water resistant. They were tested by putting them at the bottom of the deep end (3 m) of a swimming pool and leaving them there for two hours.

a) For each model, work out what fraction of the number tested, leaked.

b) Express these practical probabilities as decimals, correct to two decimal places if necessary.

c) If you go swimming wearing a Model A watch, what is the probability that it will leak?

8. One thousand "Brite" light bulbs were tested to find out how long they lasted. This pie chart shows the fractions of the bulbs that failed in a given time.

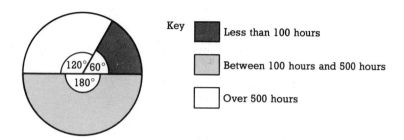

a) What fraction of the light bulbs lasted for less than 100 hours?

b) What fraction of the bulbs lasted for more than 500 hours?

c) If I buy a "Brite" bulb, what is the probability that it will last for
   i) less than 100 hours,   ii) more than 500 hours?

9. Over a six-month period the daily takings at the school tuck shop varied from less than £5 to over £50. The treasurer decided to count up the days when the takings were between certain chosen values. The pie chart shows the fractions of the days over the six-month period when the daily takings were in each of the chosen groups.

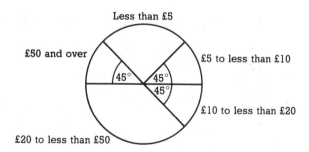

a) On what fraction of the days were the takings less than £5?

b) What is the probability that the takings tomorrow will be more than £50?

c) On what fraction of the days were the takings less than £20?

d) What is the probability that the takings tomorrow will be more than £20?

PRACTICAL PROBABILITY AND THEORETICAL PROBABILITY

We have said that, when tossing a coin, the probability of getting a head is $\frac{1}{2}$. We are basing this claim on the theory that getting a head is one of two equally likely events. We are giving a *theoretical* probability.

On the other hand, if we read that the probability of a car body rusting through within 10 years is 0·25, this is a practical probability that is based on the result of a survey (unless it is a guess, in which case it is neither theoretical nor practical).

The next exercise shows how practical results and theoretical results relate to each other.

EXERCISE 17g   **1.** You know the theoretical probability of getting a head when you toss a coin. If you toss a coin 10 times, how many times do you think that you will get a head?

2. Toss a coin ten times and record the results in a table, e.g.

Results	Number of heads so far	Number of tosses so far	Practical probability so far
HTTTHH TTTT	3	10	0.3
HTTHHTHHTH	9	20	0.45

3. Repeat Question 1 until you have tossed the coin 100 times.

4. Now plot your results on a graph like this one.

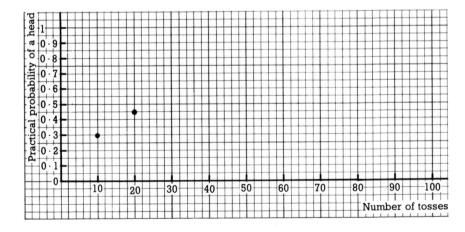

5. What is happening to the practical probability of getting a head as the number of tosses increases?

6. If you toss a coin 10 times, will it land head up five times?

7. If you roll a dice, what is the probability that you will get a 6? If you roll a dice 60 times, how many times will you get a 6?

Design an experiment like the coin tossing one, to see what happens to the practical probability of rolling a six as the number of rolls increases. Do six rolls at a time.

8. If you were doing a survey from which you hoped to work out the probability that the next car passing your home was made in Japan, how many cars should you record in your survey? Would ten cars give a reasonable prediction?

9. You suspect that the dice you are using to play a game is biased so that it does not produce as many sixes as you would expect.
Describe how you could test your suspicion.

10. Put a small piece of plasticine on one side of a 10 p coin. Find the probability of tossing a head with this coin.

18 GRAPHS

READING A TEMPERATURE CHART

When Adam went into hospital, his temperature was taken every hour and recorded on this chart.

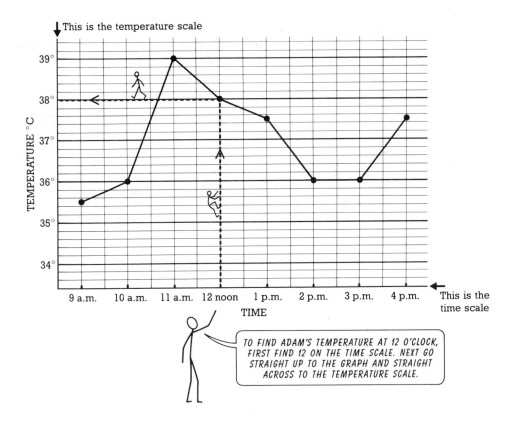

↓ This is the temperature scale

TO FIND ADAM'S TEMPERATURE AT 12 O'CLOCK, FIRST FIND 12 ON THE TIME SCALE. NEXT GO STRAIGHT UP TO THE GRAPH AND STRAIGHT ACROSS TO THE TEMPERATURE SCALE.

EXERCISE 18a 1. What was Adam's temperature at 2 p.m.?

2. What was Adam's temperature at 9 a.m.?

3. To find when Adam's temperature was 39°, first find 39° on the temperature scale. Then go across and see if there is a dot on the grid. There is one, so now go straight down to the time scale. What time was it when Adam's temperature was 39°?

172

4. Adam's temperature was recorded as 36° at three times during the day. What were these three times?

5. Can you tell what Adam's temperature was at 3.30 p.m.? Give a reason for your answer.

6. Did Adam's temperature go up or down between 10 a.m. and 11 a.m.?

7. During which hour did Adam's temperature drop by the greatest amount? What was the drop in temperature in this hour?

DRAWING A TEMPERATURE CHART

When Winston had flu, his mother took his temperature each day at 6 p.m. This is a record of his temperature.

Time	6 p.m. Monday	6 p.m. Tuesday	6 p.m. Wednesday	6 p.m. Thursday	6 p.m. Friday	6 p.m. Saturday
Temperature °C	39	40	38·5	38	37	36·5

EXERCISE 18b The diagram on the right shows part of the graph to be drawn with one point marked.

1. Draw a time scale about 8 cm from the top of a sheet of graph paper.
Mark the days of the week at 2 cm intervals.

2. Draw the temperature scale up the sheet. Use 1 cm for 1 °C. Start at 34 and continue the scale to 41.

3. Mark a dot on the graph at the given temperature for each day.

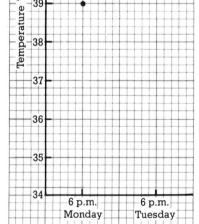

4. Join the dots with straight lines.

Now use your graph to answer the questions on the next page.

5. Between which two days did his temperature drop by the greatest amount?

6. What was this drop in temperature?

7. Can you tell from this graph what his temperature was on Wednesday morning? Give a reason for your answer.

8. Give a reason why using a curved line through the dots would give the wrong impression.

9. Why do we use straight lines to join the dots?

READING A CONTINUOUS TEMPERATURE GRAPH

This graph is a record of the outside temperature on the science block roof one day during last term.

The record was made in the school weather station on a machine that measures and records the temperature all the time. This means that we can get a continuous curved line without any dots.

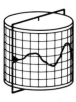

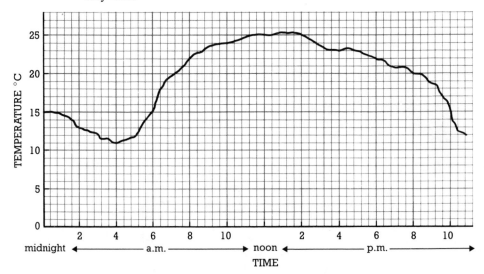

EXERCISE 18c   1. What was the temperature at 10 o'clock in the morning?

2. What was the temperature at midday?

3. Can you tell from this graph what the temperature was at 9 a.m.?

4. What was the highest temperature recorded during the day?

5. In which season of the year do you think that this record was made? Give a reason.

6. At what time of the day was the temperature highest?

7. What was the lowest temperature recorded?

8. What was the time when the temperature was lowest?

9. During which two-hour period did the temperature rise most?

10. Was the temperature rising or falling between 4 a.m. and 6 a.m.?

READING A STEP GRAPH

This graph shows the inland second-class postal charges (July 1990) for letters of different weights. The solid circle at the righthand end of each line shows that the point is part of that line. The open circle at the other end of each line shows that this point is not part of the line.

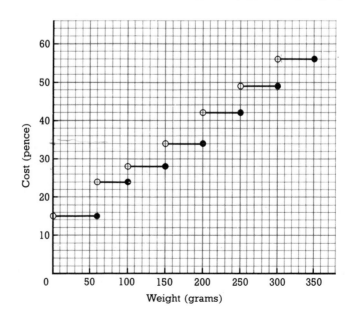

EXERCISE 18d

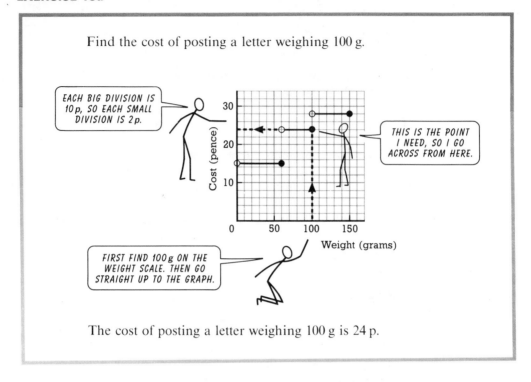

Find the cost of posting a letter weighing 100 g.

The cost of posting a letter weighing 100 g is 24 p.

Use the graph to find the cost of posting a letter weighing

1. 50 g   **3.** 210 g   **5.** 150 g   **7.** 95 g

2. 180 g   **4.** 30 g   **6.** 60 g   **8.** 250 g

READING CONVERSION GRAPHS

Conversion graphs are very useful for changing from one system of units to another. The graph opposite can be used to convert money in pounds sterling (£) to US dollars ($) and vice-versa.

EXERCISE 18e Use the conversion graph opposite to answer these questions.

1. Find the cost in pounds of a game sold in the US for $30. (The guide lines for this are marked on the graph.)

2. What is the cost in dollars of a bottle of wine priced at £8 in the UK?

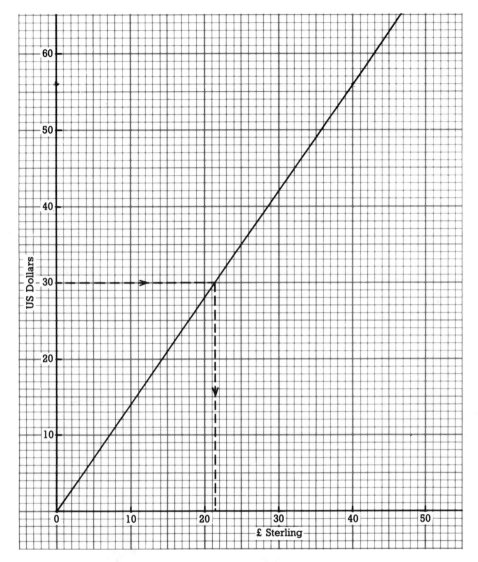

3. Find the equivalent in US dollars of
   a) £40   b) £25   c) £15.

4. Find the equivalent in £ sterling of
   a) $18   b) $60   c) $45.

5. The exchange rate gives the number of dollars that are exchanged for £1. What was the exchange rate when this graph was drawn?

This graph converts between temperature in degrees Celsius and in degrees Fahrenheit. Use the graph to answer Questions 6 to 15.

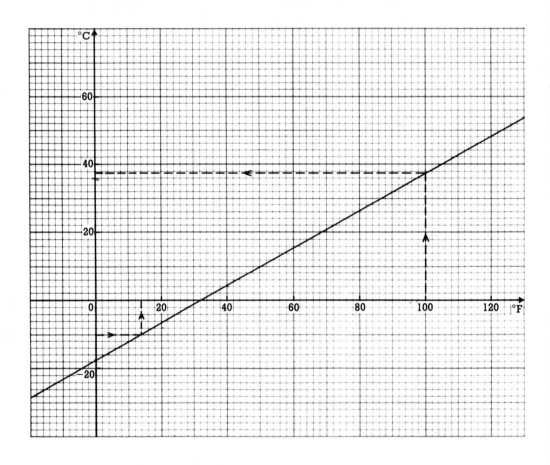

6. Use the lines drawn on the graph to convert

a) a temperature of 100 °F to °C.

b) a temperature of −10 °C to °F.

THE GUIDE LINES FOR THIS QUESTION ARE ON THE GRAPH.

7. On a warm summer day the temperature was 23 °C. What is this in °F?

8. On a cold day in winter, the temperature was 40 °F. What is this in °C?

9. The freezing point of water is 0 °C. What is the freezing point of water in °F?

10. What is 0 °F in °C?

11. One day the temperature rose from 40 °F to 60 °F.
By how many degrees Celsius did the temperature rise?

12. At 9 a.m. the temperature was 50 °F. Over the next 3 hours it rose 11 °F.
What was the temperature at 12 a.m.
a) in °F   b) in °C?

13. In the evening the temperature was 50 °F. The temperature dropped during the night by 20 °C
What did the temperature drop to
a) in °C   b) in °F?

14. The thermometer shows that the temperature is 30 °F.
a) What is the temperature in °C?
b) Is the temperature above or below the freezing point of water?

15. Normal body temperature is about 98 °F.
What is this in °C?

DRAWING CONVERSION GRAPHS

A conversion graph is a straight line. This line usually goes through the point where the two axes meet (the only exception to this rule that you are likely to come across is the graph used to convert between °C and °F).

To draw a conversion graph between Spanish pesetas and £ sterling we need the exchange rate. We will use £1 ≡ 230 pesetas.
(The symbol "≡" means "is equivalent to".)

We start by drawing axes:

the pounds axis goes across the page about 1 cm from the bottom
edge,
and the pesetas axis goes up the page about 1 cm from the left-hand
edge.

We then scale the axes:
for this graph we use 2 cm for £1 and 1 cm for 100 pesetas.

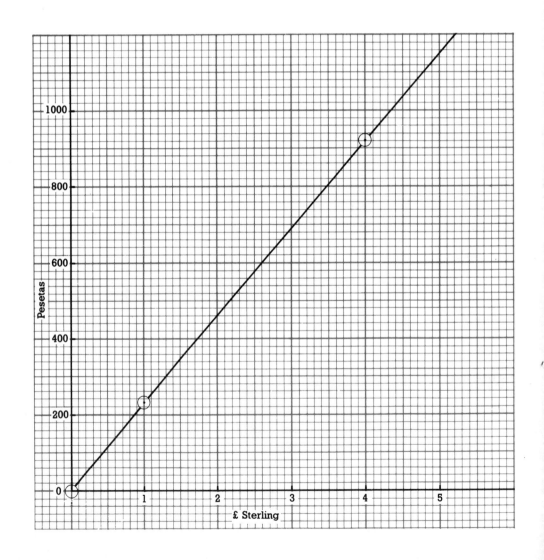

Next we plot some points. The line goes through the point where the scales cross (because £0 = 0 pesetas), so we plot that point. Next we use the exchange rate to plot the point where £1 gives 230 pesetas.

These points are too close to give an accurate line, so we use the exchange rate to work out another point.

$$£1 = 230 \text{ pesetas}, \qquad \text{so} \qquad £4 = 4 \times 230 \text{ pesetas}$$
$$= 920 \text{ pesetas}$$

Lastly we draw a line through the three points.

IF YOUR LINE DOES
NOT GO THROUGH
ALL THREE POINTS,
CHECK YOUR WORKING.

EXERCISE 18f **1.**   a) Make your own copy of the graph to convert between £ sterling and Spanish pesetas. Use the same exchange rate but continue the scales to the edges of your sheet of graph paper.
  b) Use your copy of the graph to give the cost in pesetas of a cassette sold in the UK for £7.50.

2.   a) Make a conversion graph between £ sterling and German marks, using the exchange rate £1 ≡ 3 marks.
Use a scale of 2 cm for £1 across the page and a scale of 1 cm for 1 mark up the page.
  b) Use your graph to find the cost in pounds of a plate sold in Germany for 15·50 marks.

3.   Use the graph you made for Question 1 of this exercise.
  a) The exchange rate for Spanish pesetas changed to £1 ≡ 250 pesetas.
Draw another line on your graph for this new exchange rate.
  b) A packet of pens in the duty-free shop is marked at £2.50. How many pesetas will it cost at the new exchange rate? Is this more or less than it would have cost at the old exchange rate?

19 INDEX NUMBERS

WRITE DOWN THE
NUMBER

100 000

DO I HAVE TO
WRITE DOWN ALL
THOSE NOUGHTS?

100 000 is a large number.

It is $10 \times 10 \times 10 \times 10 \times 10$, i.e. five 10s multiplied together, so we can write it as 10^5, and say "ten to the five".

In the same way, $4 \times 4 \times 4 \times 4 \times 4 \times 4$ is written as 4^6, because there are six 4s to be multiplied together.
We say "four to the six".

The 5 in 10^5 and the 6 in 4^6 are called *index numbers*. They are *not* ordinary numbers.

EXERCISE 19a

Write $2 \times 2 \times 2 \times 2 \times 2$ in index form.

$2 \times 2 \times 2 \times 2 \times 2 = 2^5$

5 IS AN INDEX NUMBER.
WE SAY "TWO TO THE FIVE".

Write in index form

1. $8 \times 8 \times 8 \times 8$

2. 9×9

3. $3 \times 3 \times 3$

4. $6 \times 6 \times 6 \times 6 \times 6 \times 6$

THIS IS NINE SQUARED.

5. $4 \times 4 \times 4 \times 4 \times 4$ **7.** $5 \times 5 \times 5 \times 5 \times 5 \times 5$

6. $7 \times 7 \times 7$ **8.** $2 \times 2 \times 2 \times 2$

Find the value of a) $2 \times 2 \times 2 \times 2$ b) 2^3

a) $2 \times 2 \times 2 \times 2 = 16$

PRESS
$2 \times 2 \times 2 \times 2 =$

b) $2^3 = 2 \times 2 \times 2$
     $= 8$

FOR 2^3 WE SAY "TWO CUBED".

---

9. Find the value of
   a) $3 \times 3 \times 3$ b) $10 \times 10 \times 10 \times 10 \times 10$ c) 5×5

Find the value of

10. 3^2 **12.** 5^3 **14.** 10^3

11. 4^4 **13.** 6^2 **15.** 2^6

16. Find the cube of 4

17. Find the square of 5

EXERCISE 19b 1.

$$4^2 = 4 \times 4$$
$$4^3 = 4 \times 4 \times 4$$
$$4^4 = 4 \times \ldots$$
$$4^5 = \ldots$$

Copy and complete this list and continue it as far as 4^7.

2. Which statement is correct?
   a) $3^2 = 6$ b) $3^2 = 9$

3. Which statement is correct?
   a) $10 \times 10 \times 10 = 10 \times 3$
   b) $10 \times 10 \times 10 = 10^3$

4. Give the value of
   a) 10×4
   b) $10 \times 10 \times 10 \times 10$
   c) 10^4

5. Give the square of
   a) 2   b) 3   c) 4

6. Give the cube of
   a) 2   b) 3   c) 4

7. Which is the bigger number, 3^4 or 4^3?

8. Write 1000 in index form.

EXERCISE 19c

Find the value of $3^2 \times 2^3$

$$3^2 = 3 \times 3$$
$$= 9$$

$$2^3 = 2 \times 2 \times 2$$
$$= 8$$

$$3^2 \times 2^3 = 9 \times 8$$
$$= 72$$

Find the value of

1. $3^2 \times 4$ **4.** 5×2^2

2. 2×4^2 **5.** $4^2 \times 2^4$

3. $3^3 \times 2^2$ **6.** 7×3^2

7. $2^4 \times 3$ **9.** $3^3 \times 2^3$

8. $6^2 \times 2^2$ **10.** $3^2 \times 2^3$

Find the value of 4×10^5

$$10^5 = 10 \times 10 \times 10 \times 10 \times 10$$
$$= 100\,000$$

THE INDEX NUMBER 5 BELONGS TO THE 10, BUT NOT TO THE 4.

$$4 \times 10^5 = 4 \times 100\,000$$
$$= 400\,000$$

Find the value of

11. 3×10^2 **14.** 2×10^3

12. 5×10^4 **15.** 2×10^5

13. 9×10^2 **16.** 7×10^9

Find the value of $1 \cdot 2 \times 10^3$

$$10^3 = 10 \times 10 \times 10$$
$$= 1000$$

$$1 \cdot 2 \times 10^3 = 1 \cdot 2 \times 1000$$
$$= 1200$$

Find the value of

17. $3 \cdot 1 \times 10^2$ **20.** $4 \cdot 2 \times 10^3$

18. $2 \cdot 5 \times 10^3$ **21.** $1 \cdot 6 \times 10^2$

19. $6 \cdot 2 \times 10^4$ **22.** $7 \cdot 4 \times 10^1$

23. $7^2 \times 2^3$

24. 6×10^3

25. $2{\cdot}8 \times 10^2$

26. $9{\cdot}1 \times 10^1$

27. 3×2^3

28. $1{\cdot}7 \times 10^3$

29. 9×10^4

30. $3{\cdot}8 \times 10^2$

SQUARE ROOTS

If we square 3 we get 9, so 9 is the *square* of 3.

Working backwards, we say that 3 is the *square root* of 9.

We write $\qquad \sqrt{9} = 3$

and read it as "the square root of 9 is 3".

EXERCISE 19d

Give   a) the square of 6   b) the square root of 36.

a) $\qquad\qquad\qquad\qquad 6^2 = 6 \times 6$

$\qquad\qquad\qquad\qquad\qquad = 36$

b) $\qquad\qquad\qquad \sqrt{36} = 6$

1. Write down

a) the square of 2
b) the square of 5.

Now write down

c) the square root of 4
d) the square root of 25.

2. Write down the square root of 16.

3. Find $\sqrt{64}$

4. Find $\sqrt{81}$

GUESS AND CHECK IN
QUESTIONS 2, 3 AND 4.

5. Hugh thought of a number and squared it. The result was 49. What was the number he thought of?

6. Susan was asked to square a number and got 100 as her answer. What was her original number?

APPROXIMATE SQUARE ROOTS

The square root of 9 is 3.
The square root of 16 is 4.

12 is between 9 and 16 so the square root of 12 will be between 3 and 4.

EXERCISE 19e

The square root of 20 lies between two whole numbers. What are these numbers?

$$3^2 = 3 \times 3 = 9 \quad \text{TOO SMALL.}$$
$$4^2 = 4 \times 4 = 16$$
$$5^2 = 5 \times 5 = 25 \quad \text{TOO BIG.}$$

20 lies between 16 and 25, so $\sqrt{20}$ lies between 4 and 5.

The square root of each of the following numbers lies between two whole numbers.

In each case, what are the two whole numbers?

1. 7	**3.** 30	**5.** 15
2. 5	**4.** 39	**6.** 45
7. 27	**9.** 22	**11.** 13
8. 10	**10.** 19	**12.** 17

Once we have found that the square root lies between two particular numbers, we can find a rough answer by more guessing and checking.

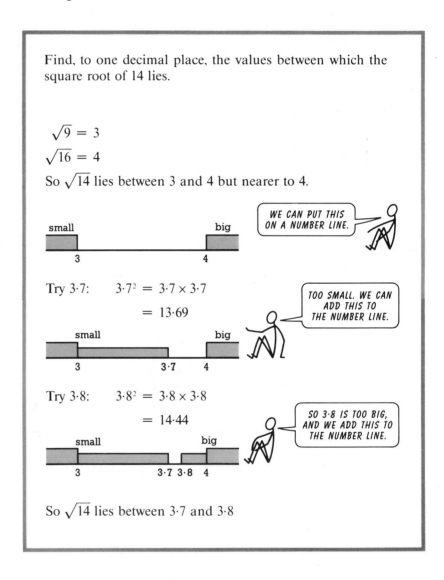

Find, to one decimal place, the values between which the square root of 14 lies.

$$\sqrt{9} = 3$$
$$\sqrt{16} = 4$$

So $\sqrt{14}$ lies between 3 and 4 but nearer to 4.

small   big

3   4

WE CAN PUT THIS ON A NUMBER LINE.

Try 3·7: $3·7^2 = 3·7 \times 3·7$
                  $= 13·69$

small   big

3   3·7   4

TOO SMALL. WE CAN ADD THIS TO THE NUMBER LINE.

Try 3·8: $3·8^2 = 3·8 \times 3·8$
                  $= 14·44$

small   big

3   3·7 3·8   4

SO 3·8 IS TOO BIG, AND WE ADD THIS TO THE NUMBER LINE.

So $\sqrt{14}$ lies between 3·7 and 3·8

Find to one decimal place, the values between which each square root lies.

13. $\sqrt{22}$ **15.** $\sqrt{13}$ **17.** $\sqrt{7}$

14. $\sqrt{10}$ **16.** $\sqrt{32}$ **18.** $\sqrt{18}$

MORE ACCURATE SQUARE ROOTS

We can find square roots more quickly by using the button on the calculator marked $\sqrt{}$

EXERCISE 19f

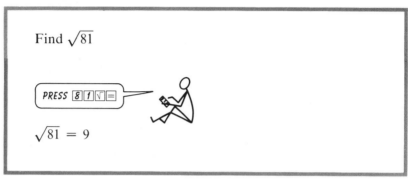

Find $\sqrt{81}$

PRESS $\boxed{8}\boxed{1}\boxed{\sqrt{}}\boxed{=}$

$\sqrt{81} = 9$

Use a calculator to find the square root of

1.	16	**4.**	100	**7.**	144
2.	36	**5.**	64	**8.**	225
3.	25	**6.**	49	**9.**	121

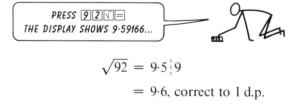

Find $\sqrt{92}$, giving the answer correct to 1 decimal place.

PRESS $\boxed{9}\boxed{2}\boxed{\sqrt{}}\boxed{=}$
THE DISPLAY SHOWS 9·59166...

$\sqrt{92} = 9·5 \vdots 9$

$= 9·6$, correct to 1 d.p.

Find, correct to 1 decimal place, the square root of

10.	6	**11.**	19	**12.**	27

Find, correct to the nearest whole number, the square root of

13.	700	**14.**	499	**15.**	1111

16. a) Find 17^2
   b) Find the square root of the answer to (a).

17. a) Find $\sqrt{529}$
   b) Find the square of the answer to (a).
      Does it agree with what you already know?

18. Copy and complete the following statement.

The _____ of 100 is 10.

19. Copy and complete the following statement.

The _____ of 5 is 25.

CUBES AND CUBE ROOTS

The cube of 4 is $4 \times 4 \times 4$, i.e. 64.

So the cube root of 64 is 4.

We can find cube roots of numbers by guessing and checking as we did with square roots.

EXERCISE 19g

Find the cube root of 216.

Try 8: $8 \times 8 \times 8 = 512$ *TOO BIG.*
Try 7: $7 \times 7 \times 7 = 343$ *STILL TOO BIG.*
Try 6: $6 \times 6 \times 6 = 216$

The cube root of 216 is 6.

Find the cube roots of the following numbers.

1. 729   **2.** 125   **3.** 1000   **4.** 27

Find, to one decimal place, the values between which the cube root of 200 lies.

Try 6: $6 \times 6 \times 6 = 216$ Too big

Try 5: $5 \times 5 \times 5 = 125$ Too small

Try 5·8: $5·8 \times 5·8 \times 5·8 = 195·112$ A bit small

Try 5·9: $5·9 \times 5·9 \times 5·9 = 205·379$ A bit big

> PUT ALL THESE ON A NUMBER LINE.

small   big

5   5·8 5·9 6

So the cube root of 200 is between 5·8 and 5·9

Find, to one decimal place, the values between which the cube root of each number lies.

5. 24 (Try 3 and 2 first.)   **6.** 97 (Try 4 and 5 first.)

7. 68   **8.** 112   **9.** 500   **10.** 160

MIXED EXERCISES

EXERCISE 19h 1. Find the value of $3 \times 3 \times 3 \times 3$

2. Find the value of 5^3

3. Which is correct, $4^3 = 12$ or $4^3 = 64$?

4. Write $2 \times 2 \times 2 \times 2 \times 2$ in index form.

5. Find $\sqrt{121}$

EXERCISE 19i 1. Find the square root of 144.

2. Find the cube of 6.

3. Write $4 \times 4 \times 4 \times 4$ in index form.

4. Find $\sqrt{72}$, correct to 1 decimal place.

5. Find the missing index number.
$$2^? = 16$$

EXERCISE 19j **1.** Find the value of $5 \times 5 \times 5 \times 5$

2. Find the value of 3^5.

3. Write $7 \times 7 \times 7 \times 7$ in index form.

4. Find $\sqrt{50}$ correct to 1 decimal place.

5. Which is correct, $6^3 = 216$ or $6^3 = 18$?

20 NUMBER PATTERNS

EXTENDING NUMBER PATTERNS

Look at these numbers   3, 5, 7, 9 . . .

Before we can add more numbers we need to find what rule is applied to each number to give the next one.

Once we see that we add 2 to each number to get the next one, we can continue the list of numbers   3, 5, 7, 9, 11, 13,   and so on.

EXERCISE 20a

Look at this list of numbers: 3, 9, 27 . . .

a) Describe what we do to each number to get the next one in the list.

b) Add two more numbers to the list.

a) 3, 9, 27 . . .

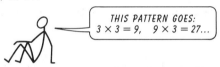

THIS PATTERN GOES:
3 × 3 = 9,   9 × 3 = 27...

We multiply each number by three to find the next one.

b) 1, 3, 9, 27, 81, 243

In each question
a) describe how to get the next number in the list
b) write down the next two numbers.

1. 1, 4, 7, 10 . . .

2. 4, 6, 8, 10 . . .

3. 1, 2, 4, 8 . . .

4. 3, 7, 11, 15 . . .

5. 2, 7, 12, 17 . . .

6. 5, 10, 20, 40 . . .

7. 14, 16, 18, 20 . . .

8. 1, 4, 16 . . .

9. 10, 30, 90 . . .

10. 7, 13, 19 . . .

For each of the following lists, describe what is done to each number to get the following number and give the next two numbers in the pattern.

a) 7, 5, 3, 1, -1...   b) 8, 4, 2, 1, $\frac{1}{2}$...

a) 7, 5, 3, 1, -1...
We subtract two from each number to get the next one.
7, 5, 3, 1, -1, -3, -5.

b) 8, 4, 2, 1, $\frac{1}{2}$...
We divide each number by two to get the next one.
8, 4, 2, 1, $\frac{1}{2}$, $\frac{1}{4}$, $\frac{1}{8}$.

In each question from 11 to 16
a) describe how to get the next number in the list
b) write down the next two numbers.

11. 90, 60, 30...   **13.** 9, 4, -1...   **15.** 2, 0, -2...

12. 64, 16, 4...   **14.** 27, 9, 3...   **16.** 20, 14, 8, 2...

17. Write down the pattern you get by starting with 3 and adding 4 each time. What is the tenth number in this pattern?

18. Write down the pattern you get by starting with 10 and subtracting 5 each time. What is the eighth number in this pattern?

19. Write down the pattern you get by starting with 1 and multiplying by 2 each time.
a) What is the sixth number in this pattern?
b) What happens if you start with 0 instead of 1?

20. Write down the numbers 1 and 2. Make a pattern using this rule: the next number you write is the sum of the two previous numbers. What is the eleventh number in this pattern?

SQUARE NUMBERS

. . . .
. . .   .
. .   . .
.   . .   .

Counting the number of dots needed to make each of these squares we get

1, 4, 9, 16.

These numbers are called *square numbers*.

EXERCISE 20b 1. Look at the dot squares above and draw the fifth square of dots.

2. What is the fifth square number?

3. What is the sixth square number?

4. Write down the next two square numbers.

5. Copy and complete this table which shows the differences between consecutive square numbers.

"CONSECUTIVE" MEANS "FOLLOWING AFTER EACH OTHER".

4 − 1	3
9 − 4	5
16 − 9	
25 − 16	
36 − 25	
49 − 36	
64 − 49	

6. What do you notice about the numbers in the last column?

7. Without writing down any more square numbers, give the next two numbers in the right-hand column.

TRIANGULAR NUMBERS ▬▬▬▬▬▬▬▬▬▬▬▬▬▬▬▬▬▬▬▬▬▬

The numbers of dots needed to make these triangles are called *triangular numbers*.

EXERCISE 20c 1. Make a list of the number of dots in each of the five triangles above.

2. Draw a sixth triangle and add the number of dots in it to your list.

3. Make a list of the differences between consecutive triangular numbers. The first two are done for you.

2, 3 . . .

4. Add one more number to the list you made in Question 3.

5. Use this number to find how many dots are needed to make the seventh triangle.
Check this number by drawing the seventh triangle.

MIXED EXERCISE ▬▬▬▬▬▬▬▬▬▬▬▬▬▬▬▬▬▬▬▬▬▬▬▬▬▬▬

EXERCISE 20d 1. Write down the numbers 1 and 2. Make a pattern using this rule: the next number in the pattern is the result of multiplying the two previous numbers together. What is the seventh number in the pattern ?

2. a) Write down the missing numbers in this number pattern

3, 9, ☐ , 21, 27, ☐ . . .

b) Copy and complete this sentence: "To get this pattern, start with 3 then . . ."

3. a) Write down the missing numbers in this pattern.

$$8, 4, 2, \boxed{}, \tfrac{1}{2}, \boxed{}, \tfrac{1}{8}, \tfrac{1}{16} \cdots$$

b) Copy and complete this sentence: "To get this pattern, start with 8 then ..."

4. Write down the missing numbers in this pattern

$$\tfrac{1}{9}, \tfrac{1}{3}, 1, \boxed{}, \boxed{}, 27, 81, 243 \ldots$$

and then copy and complete the sentence: "To get this pattern, start with $\tfrac{1}{9}$ and ..."

5.
$$
\begin{array}{ccccc}
 & 1 & 2 & & \\
 1 & 2 & 2 & & \\
 1 & 2 & 4 & 2 & \\
1 & 2 & 8 & 8 & 2 \\
\end{array}
$$

Try to find a pattern in these rows of numbers. Write down the next row.

6. Make up a rule of your own for forming a number pattern. Give it to your neighbour and see if he/she gets the pattern you had in mind.

7. Draw the next two diagrams for this pattern.

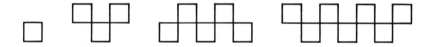

How many squares are used to make

a) the fifth diagram in the pattern

b) the eighth diagram in the pattern?

8. Draw the next three diagrams for this pattern.

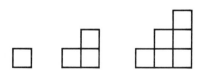

How many squares are used to make

a) the fifth diagram in the pattern

b) the ninth diagram in the pattern?

21 FORMULAE

USING A FUNCTION MACHINE

There is a rule for changing numbers in the top row of this table to the numbers in the bottom row.

$$
\begin{array}{ccccc}
1 & 3 & 6 & 9 & 12 \\
\downarrow & \downarrow & \downarrow & \downarrow & \downarrow \\
5 & 7 & 10 & 13 & 16
\end{array}
$$

This function machine gives that rule:

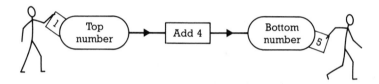

If the letter a stands for the number in the top row and the letter b stands for the number in the bottom row, we can use symbols in the function machine, i.e.

The instruction "+4" means "add on 4".

EXERCISE 21a 1. Copy this table.

$$
\begin{array}{c|cccccc}
x & 1 & 2 & 3 & 4 & 8 & 12 \\
\hline
 & \downarrow & \downarrow & & & & \\
y & 4 & 5 & & & &
\end{array}
$$

Use this function machine to complete your table.

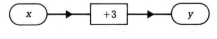

198

2. Copy this table.

$$\begin{array}{c|ccccccc} x & 1 & 2 & 3 & 4 & 5 & 10 & 12 \\ \hline & \downarrow & \downarrow & & & & & \\ y & 0 & 1 & & & & & \end{array}$$

Use this function machine to complete your table.

3. a) Copy the table. Then use the function machine to complete your table.

$$\begin{array}{c|ccccc} x & 2 & 4 & 5 & 8 & 20 \\ \hline & \downarrow & & & & \\ y & 6 & & & & \end{array}$$

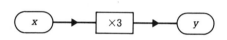

b) If x is 10, what is y?

c) What is y when x is 3?

4. a) Copy the table and use the function machine to complete it.

$$\begin{array}{c|cccccc} p & 1 & 2 & 3 & 4 & 5 & 6 \\ \hline & \downarrow & \downarrow & & & & \\ A & 1 & 4 & & & & \end{array}$$

b) If p is 10, what is A?

c) If p is 8, what is A?

A SHORTER FORM OF FUNCTION MACHINE

We use symbols in function machines because they are quicker to write than instructions in words. It takes some time to write down a function machine even using symbols, so we look at ways of shortening this.

Here is the start of a function machine.

This tells us that we put in a number and then multiply it by 2.

We can write this instruction as $x \times 2$

or $2 \times x$

or even more briefly as $2x$

WE WRITE THE NUMBER FIRST.

$2x$ means *multiply 2 by the number that x stands for.*

This short form is called an *algebraic expression.*

EXERCISE 21b

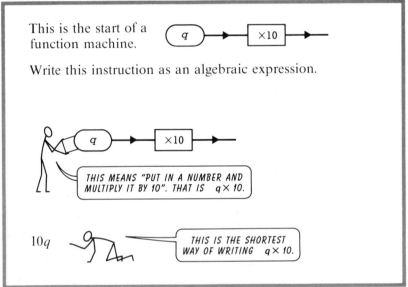

This is the start of a function machine.

q → $\times 10$ →

Write this instruction as an algebraic expression.

q → $\times 10$ →

THIS MEANS "PUT IN A NUMBER AND MULTIPLY IT BY 10". THAT IS $q \times 10$.

$10q$

THIS IS THE SHORTEST WAY OF WRITING $q \times 10$.

Each question gives the start of a function machine. Write down the instruction as an algebraic expression.

1. x → $\times 3$ →   **4.** p → $\times 3$ →

2. x → $\times 4$ →   **5.** x → $\times 5$ →

3. a → $\times 2$ →   **6.** t → $\times 6$ →

The start of another function machine is

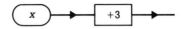

This tells us to put in a number x and then add 3 to it.

We can write this instruction as

$$x + 3$$

There is *no shorter way* of writing this.

EXERCISE 21c Write each of these instructions as an algebraic expression.

1.    **4.**

2.   **5.**

3.    **6.**

7. 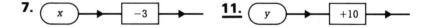   **11.**

8.   **12.**

9.   **13.**

10.   **14.**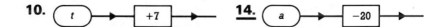

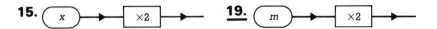

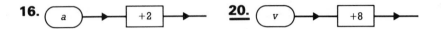

15. (x)──▶[×2]──▶   **19.** (m)──▶[×2]──▶

16. (a)──▶[+2]──▶   **20.** (v)──▶[+8]──▶

17. (t)──▶[×10]──▶   **21.** (x)──▶[+9]──▶

18. (x)──▶[÷2]──▶   **22.** (u)──▶[÷3]──▶

FORMULAE

This is a complete function machine.

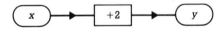

This tells us to put in a number x and then add 2 to it, giving us the output number y. We can write this as $x + 2 \longrightarrow y$

This means that $x + 2$ gives y

Using algebra, we write this as

$$x + 2 = y$$

or $$y = x + 2$$

This is the shortest way of writing this function machine. We call it a *formula*. The plural of formula is *formulae*.

EXERCISE 21d

Write each function machine as a formula.

a)

a ⟶ ×3 ⟶ b

THIS MEANS "PUT IN a AND MULTIPLY BY 3 TO GIVE b".

b)

a ⟶ −2 ⟶ b

a) $3a = b$ or $b = 3a$

b) $a - 2 = b$ or $b = a - 2$

Write each function machine as a formula.

1. x ⟶ ×3 ⟶ y

2. p ⟶ +3 ⟶ q

3. s ⟶ ×2 ⟶ t

4. a ⟶ +1 ⟶ b

5. x ⟶ −5 ⟶ y

6. p ⟶ ×6 ⟶ r

USING FORMULAE

We can use a formula just as we use a function machine.

EXERCISE 21e

Copy this table.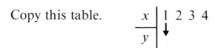

Use the formula $y = x + 3$ to complete the table.

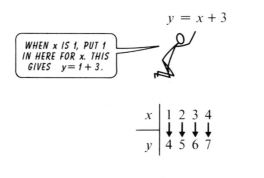

Copy the table and use the formula to complete it.

1. x | 1 2 3 4 5 $y = 3x$
        —————↓
         y |

2. x | 1 2 3 4 5 $y = x - 1$
        —————↓
         y |

3. s | 1 2 3 4 5 $t = 4s$
        —————↓
         t |

4. a | 1 2 3 4 5
         $\dfrac{}{b}$ ↓ $b = a + 2$

5. t | 1 2 3 4 5
         $\dfrac{}{p}$ ↓ $p = t + 4$

6. w | 1 2 3 4 5
         $\dfrac{}{t}$ ↓ $t = 5w$

7.   What is y if $y = x + 2$, and x is 3?

8. $3a = b$. If a is 2, what is b?

9.   With this formula we can work out how long it takes to cook a loaf of bread.

$$t = 20w$$

w is the number of pounds that the uncooked loaf weighs and t is the number of minutes it takes to cook.

a) How many minutes are needed to cook a loaf weighing 2 lb?
b) How long should a loaf weighing 3 lb take to cook?
c) If the loaf weighs one and a half pounds, how many minutes will it take to cook?

10. This formula can be used to work out the money made from selling bags of popcorn.

$$P = 15n$$

n is the number of bags of popcorn sold and P is the number of pence collected.

a) How much money is collected when 10 bags of popcorn are sold?
b) What sum of money is taken when 200 bags are sold?
c) How many bags need to be sold to make £3?
d) What is the cost of one bag of popcorn?

FORMULAE WITH TWO OPERATIONS

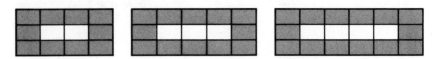

This function machine works out the number of grey tiles in the pattern when the number of white tiles is known.

w is the number of white tiles and g is the number of grey tiles.

This tells us that we have to multiply w by 2 and then add 6 to get g. These instructions can be written in one formula as

$$g = 2w + 6$$

We can check that this is correct by testing it on the second pattern. There are 3 white tiles so $w = 3$

$$\text{Then} \quad g = 2 \times 3 + 6$$
$$= 6 + 6$$
$$= 12$$

and we see that there *are* 12 grey tiles.

EXERCISE 21f

> If 8 white tiles are used, use the formula $g = 2w + 6$ to find the number of grey tiles needed.
>
>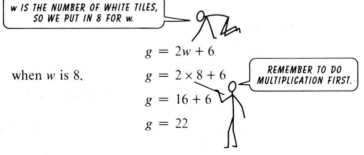
>
> *w* IS THE NUMBER OF WHITE TILES, SO WE PUT IN 8 FOR *w*.
>
> when w is 8,
> $$g = 2w + 6$$
> $$g = 2 \times 8 + 6$$
> $$g = 16 + 6$$
> $$g = 22$$
>
> REMEMBER TO DO MULTIPLICATION FIRST.
>
> g is the number of grey tiles, so 22 grey tiles are needed.

Use the formula $g = 2w + 6$ to answer these questions.

1. If 6 white tiles are used, how many grey tiles are needed?

2. When the pattern has 4 white tiles, how many grey tiles does it have?

3. How many grey tiles are needed when 5 white tiles are used?

4. If w is 10, what is g?

5. What is g when w is 20?

With the formula given below we can work out the cost of taking some children to a theatre.

$$C = 3n - 1$$

n is the number of children and C is the number of pounds that it costs. Use this formula to answer the questions below.

6. If 10 children go, how much does it cost?

7. What is the cost if 20 children go?

8. What does it cost to take 6 children?

9. If n is 4, what is C?

10. What is C when n is 12?

11. Copy the table and then complete it, using the formula
$y = 5x - 3$

x	1	3	6	8	9	12
y						

FORMULAE WITH TWO INPUTS

The area of a rectangle is found by multiplying the length by the width.

If *l* stands for the *number* of units of length, and *b* stands for the *number* of units of width, then the instruction for finding the area tells us to multiply *l* by *b*.

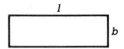

$l \times b$ is written as lb

If *A* stands for the number of units of area, we can write the instruction for finding the area as the formula

$$A = lb$$

To find *A*, we need to put in two numbers, one for *l* and one for *b*.

EXERCISE 21g

Use the formula $A = lb$ to find the area of a rectangle which is 6 cm long and 4 cm wide.

I IS THE NUMBER OF CENTIMETRES OF LENGTH, SO WE PUT 6 FOR l.

b IS THE NUMBER OF CENTIMETRES OF WIDTH, SO WE PUT 4 FOR b.

$A = lb$

$A = 6 \times 4$

$A = 24$

The area is 24 cm²

Use the formula $A = lb$ to find *A* when

1. *l* is 5 and *b* is 2

2. *l* is 8 and *b* is 3

3. *l* is 10 and *b* is 3

4. *l* is 9 and *b* is 2

5. If the length of a rectangle is 12 cm and its width is 4 cm, what is its area ?

6. Find the area of a rectangle measuring 7 cm by 4 cm.

7. The formula which gives
the perimeter of a rectangle
is

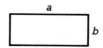

$$p = 2a + 2b$$

where p is the number of units of length all the way round, a is the number of units in the length of each long side and b is the number of units in the length of each short side.

a) Find p when a is 4 and b is 3.

b) What is p when a is 5 and b is 6?

c) A rectangle measures 2 cm by 3 cm. Use the formula to find its perimeter.

d) Use the formula to find the perimeter of a rectangle that is 8 cm long and 6 cm wide.

If $a = 2b - c$, what is a when b is 3 and c is 4?

PUT 3 FOR b, AND 4 FOR c.

$$a = 2b - c$$

$$a = 2 \times 3 - 4$$

REMEMBER TO MULTIPLY FIRST.

$$a = 6 - 4$$

$$a = 2$$

---

8. If $p = 3q + r$, what is p when

a) q is 2 and r is 4

b) q is 5 and r is 3?

9. If $s = t - u$, find s when

a) t is 8 and u is 2

b) t is 4 and u is 3.

10. Given that $a = bc - 3$, find a when

a) b is 5 and c is 2

b) b is 6 and c is 3.

11.   Use the formula $v = u + 10t$ to find v when
    a) $u = 2$ and $t = 2$ b) $u = 5$ and $t = 3$.

12.   If $C = nt + n$ find C when
    a) $n = 4$ and $t = 2$ b) $n = 5$ and $t = 3$.

13.   Given that $P = 2v - t$,   find P when
    a) $v = 5$ and $t = 2$ b) $v = 9$ and $t = 4$.

14.   If $I = mv$,   find I when
    a) $m = 1\cdot5$ and $v = 2\cdot4$ b) $m = 2\cdot6$ and $v = 0\cdot5$.

15.   Use the formula $I = 0\cdot1 \times PT$ to find I when
    a) $P = 50$ and $T = 0\cdot5$ b) $P = 10$ and $T = 1\cdot5$.

22 CIRCLES

DRAWING CIRCLES

The edge of a circle is called the *circumference*.

A portion of the circumference is called an *arc*.

All points on the circumference are the same distance from the *centre*.

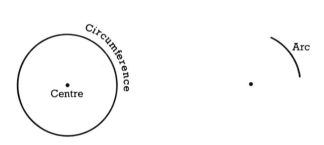

A line drawn from the centre to the circumference is a *radius*.

A line drawn through the centre from edge to edge, is a *diameter*.

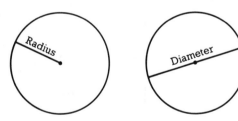

We use a pair of compasses to draw a circle accurately.

The distance between the pencil point and the point of the compasses gives the radius of the circle.

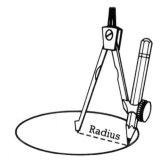

EXERCISE 22a The patterns drawn in these questions are not full size. You will need more space when you draw your pattern using the radius given in the question.

1. Draw a circle with a radius of 5 cm. Draw a radius and a diameter, then label your drawing with the words *centre*, *radius*, *diameter* and *circumference*.

For Questions 2, 3 and 4, use 1 cm squared paper.

2. Mark four points at the corners of a square whose sides are 4 cm long.
    Take each of the corners as the centre of a circle and draw the pattern show below.

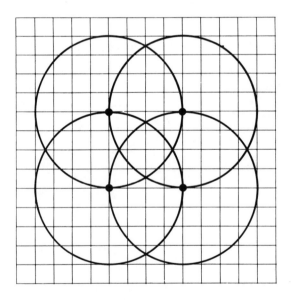

3. Start by drawing a wavy line, leaving plenty of space above and below it. With your compass point at the end of the line, draw a circle of radius 4 cm. Without changing the radius, move the point 2 cm along the line and draw another circle.

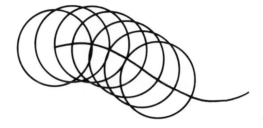

Continue like this until you get to the end of the line.

4. To draw this pattern, start with the circle in the middle and use 4 cm for the radius.

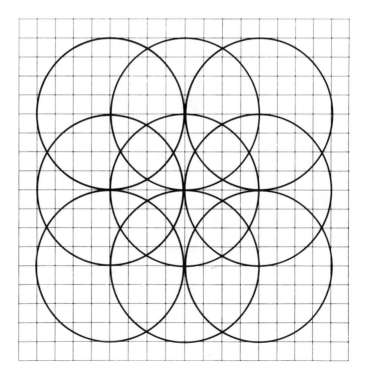

5. Mark two points, A and B,
6 cm apart. Leave plenty of
room above AB for the circles
shown in the diagram below.
Taking A as the centre and
using a radius of 6 cm,
draw an arc above AB.
Repeat this using B as the
centre. Mark the point C
where the two arcs cross

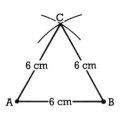

(C should not be exactly on the corner of a grid square).
Now draw three circles, each with a radius of 3 cm, to form
the pattern in the diagram. If you draw it well the circles will
just touch.

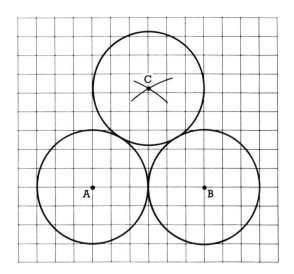

6. Use plain paper to draw this
pattern.
Start by drawing the circle
in the middle, using a radius
of 4 cm. Take any point on
this circle as your centre and
draw another circle with the
same radius.
Can you see what to do next?

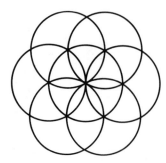

DIAMETER AND RADIUS

EXERCISE 22b 1. Measure the radius and the diameter of each circle, to the nearest millimetre. Make a copy of the table given below and record your measurements in the table.

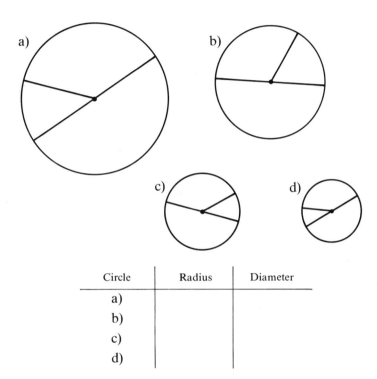

Circle	Radius	Diameter
a)		
b)		
c)		
d)		

What do you notice?

> The diameter of a circle is twice as long as the radius.

Use this fact to answer the following questions.

2. The radius of a lifebelt is 40 cm. What is its diameter?

3. The diameter of a round coffee table is 64 cm. What is its radius?

4. What is the diameter of a bicycle wheel with a radius of 25 cm?

5. The radius of an LP record is 15 cm. What is its diameter?

CIRCUMFERENCE AND DIAMETER

EXERCISE 22c For this exercise you need four or five circular objects, e.g. a cola can, a plate, a saucer, a roll of sticky tape, a 10 p coin, a cocoa tin. You also need a copy of this table and a tape measure.

Object	Diameter	Circumference
a)		
b)		
c)		
d)		
e)		

1. Take your first object; the can for example. Measure the diameter of the can to the nearest millimetre and write it in your table.

REMEMBER THAT THE DIAMETER GOES THROUGH THE MIDDLE.

Then measure the distance *round* the can with a tape measure and write it in the circumference column of your table.

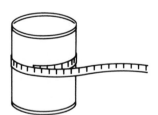

2. Do the same with each of your other objects, writing all your measurements in the table.

3. Decide from the numbers in your table which of these statements is *roughly* true.
a) Distance round $= 2 \times$ Diameter
b) Distance round $= 3 \times$ Diameter
c) Distance round $= 4 \times$ Diameter

You should have found that the circumference of a circle is just over three times the diameter. So we can find a rough value for the circumference if we use

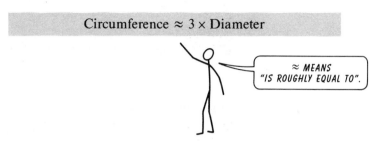

Circumference ≈ 3 × Diameter

≈ *MEANS*
"IS ROUGHLY EQUAL TO".

EXERCISE 22d In this exercise you will need to use

Diameter is twice radius

and   Circumference ≈ 3 × Diameter

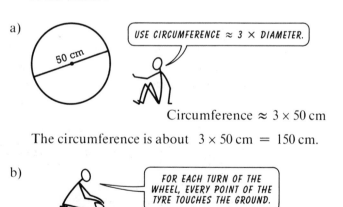

The diameter of Tom's bicycle wheel is 50 centimetres.

a) What, approximately, is the circumference of the wheel?

b) About how far forward does Tom move for each turn of the wheel?

a)

50 cm

USE CIRCUMFERENCE ≈ 3 × DIAMETER.

Circumference ≈ 3 × 50 cm

The circumference is about   3 × 50 cm = 150 cm.

b)

FOR EACH TURN OF THE WHEEL, EVERY POINT OF THE TYRE TOUCHES THE GROUND.

Tom moves forward about 150 cm.

1.   The diameter of a 2 p coin is about 25 mm. What is its circumference approximately?

2. Rachel takes the label off this tin.
About how long is it?

3. a) About how far does the tip of the minute hand of this clock move in one hour?

b) About how far does the tip of the hour hand move in twelve hours?

THE TIP OF THE HAND GOES ROUND IN A CIRCLE.

4. The diameter of a car wheel is 45 cm. Roughly how far forward does the car move for each turn of the wheel?

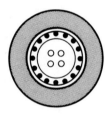

The distance round an oak tree is measured. If it is 180 cm, what, approximately, is the diameter of the tree?

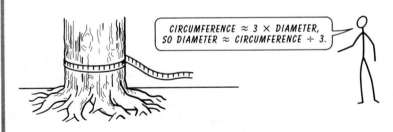

CIRCUMFERENCE ≈ 3 × DIAMETER, SO DIAMETER ≈ CIRCUMFERENCE ÷ 3.

Diameter ≈ Circumference ÷ 3

Diameter ≈ 180 ÷ 3

The diameter of the tree is about 60 cm.

5. Laura walks right round this pond. If she has walked 15 metres, what is the approximate diameter of the pond?

6. John attached a trim to the edge of a round table. If he used 300 cm of the trim, find the approximate diameter of the table.

7. Gita runs once round a circular running track. If she has run 240 m, about what is the diameter of the track?

8. Gemma wants to bind the edge of a round rug of diameter 90 cm. If she allows for the binding to overlap by 10 cm, about what length of binding does Gemma need?

9. Aziz measures the diameter of a coin and finds it to be 22 mm. Approximately how far is it around the edge of the coin?

FINDING THE CIRCUMFERENCE MORE ACCURATELY ▬▬▬

We already know that the circumference is *about* three times the diameter, but this is a very rough approximation.

A true value of the circumference is given when we multiply the diameter by a number which is called "pi" and is written π

If you press the π button on your calculator you will find that the display shows 3·1415927 (or even more figures on some calculators). Instead of writing down all these figures, we use the symbol π whenever we want to write down the accurate link between circumference and diameter.

If we also use the abbreviations C for circumference and D for diameter, then we can write $C = \pi \times D$

i.e. $$C = \pi D$$

EXERCISE 22e In this exercise use the π button on your calculator and give your answers correct to the nearest centimetre (or metre where this is the unit in the question). If your calculator does not have a π button, use 3·14 for π.

The diameter of a bicycle wheel is 50 cm. What is the distance round the rim?

$C = \pi D$

$C = \pi \times 50$ $\left(\boxed{\pi} \boxed{\times} \boxed{5} \boxed{0} \boxed{=} \right)$

THE DISPLAY GIVES 157·07, BUT I WANT THE NEAREST WHOLE NUMBER.

$= 157$

The wheel rim is 157 cm correct to the nearest centimetre.

---

1. The diameter of a dustbin is 48 cm. What is the distance round the bin?

2. Gemma's frisbee has a diameter of 23 cm. What is its circumference?

3. Rajiv walked straight across the middle of a circular lawn while Kathy walked all around the edge. If the distance that Rajiv walked was 12 m, how far did Kathy walk?

4. A round dining table has a *radius* of 60 cm. Find its circumference.

5. The radius of the centre circle on a football pitch is 9 m. What is the circumference?

6. A Christmas cake with a diameter of 24 cm has a red ribbon wrapped around it for decoration. If the ends of the ribbon overlap by 3 cm, what is the length of the ribbon?

7. Go back to Exercise 22d and find more accurate answers to Questions 1 to 4.

23 SOLIDS

CUBOIDS

EXERCISE 23a 1.

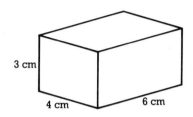

This is a picture of a cuboid or rectangular block.

Each face is a *rectangle*.

Below is a *net* of this cuboid.

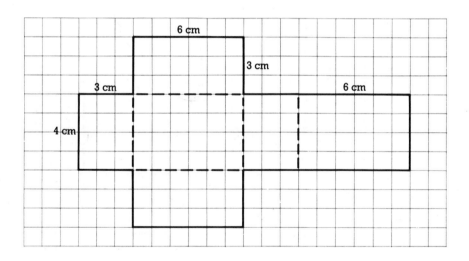

a) Draw the net full size on squared paper and cut it out. Fold it along the broken lines and fix it together with sticky tape to make the cuboid.

b) What is the shape of each face?

c) How many faces are there on the cuboid?

d) How many edges does it have?

2. Below are several different arrangements of rectangles. Each square represents a square of side 1 cm.

    Some of them are nets of the cuboid in Question 1, but some of them will not fold up to make the cuboid.

    Draw them and try making them up. Which of them will make the cuboid?

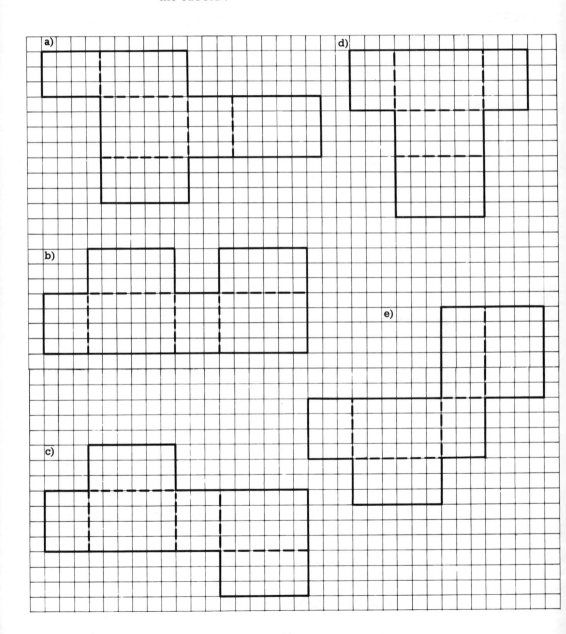

3.

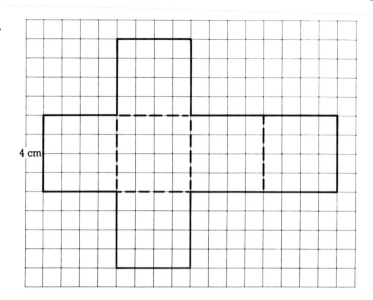

a) Above is the net of a cube. Copy the net full size on squared paper and make the solid.

b) What is the shape of each face?

c) How many faces are there on the cube?

d) How many edges does it have?

e) Compare your answers with those in Question 1. What do you notice?

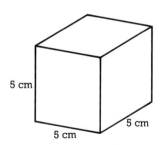

REMEMBER THAT A CUBE IS A CUBOID, THOUGH A SPECIAL ONE.

4.

5 cm

5 cm

5 cm

Draw a net of this cube and make it up.

5. Below are several different arrangements of six squares. Some of them can be used as nets of cubes but one at least will not fold up into a cube.
Draw them and try making them up. Which of them will make a cube?

a)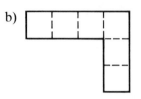

d)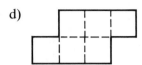

b)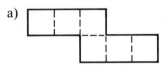

e)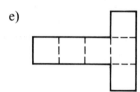

c)

f) Now draw other arrangements of six squares and try them out.

VOLUME

The volume of this cube is 1 cubic centimetre, or 1 cm³.

A 1 cm cube

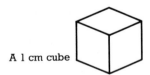

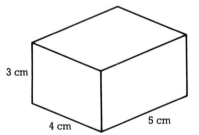

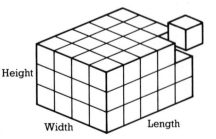

We can work out the volume of this cuboid by filling it with 1 cm cubes and counting the cubes.

We can also see that we find the
number of cubes if we multiply
length by width by height.

*"BREADTH" IS SOMETIMES USED
INSTEAD OF "WIDTH".*

> The volume of a cuboid = Length × Width × Height.

We can write this in the form of a formula:

$$V = L \times W \times H$$

EXERCISE 23b

Find the volume of this cuboid.

3 cm

4 cm   6 cm

Volume = Length × Width × Height

$= 6 \times 4 \times 3$ cm^3

$= 72$ cm^3

*DON'T FORGET
THE UNITS.*

*WE COULD HAVE USED
$V = L \times W \times H$.*

1. Find the volume of each of these two cuboids.

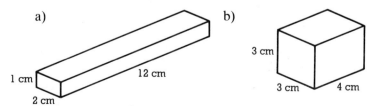

a)

1 cm

2 cm   12 cm

b)

3 cm

3 cm   4 cm

c) Which cuboid has the bigger volume?

2. a)

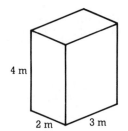

4 m

2 m   3 m

b)

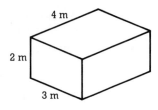

4 m

2 m

3 m

Which cuboid has the bigger volume?

3. Find the volume of a cuboid which measures 5 cm by 6 cm by 7 cm.

4.

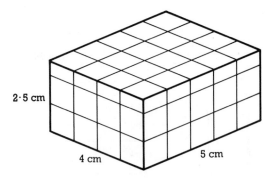

2·5 cm

4 cm   5 cm

a) How many cubes are there in the bottom layer?

b) To make the top layer we need to cut the 1 cm cubes in half.

Cube   Half-cube

What is the volume of a half-cube?

c) How many half-cubes are there in the top layer?

d) What is the volume of the top layer?

e) What is the volume of the whole cuboid?

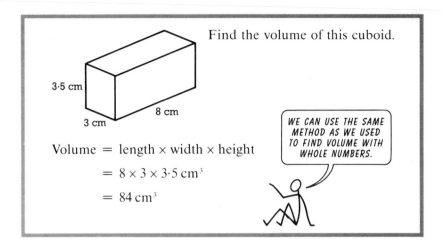

Find the volume of this cuboid.

3·5 cm

8 cm

3 cm

Volume = length × width × height

WE CAN USE THE SAME METHOD AS WE USED TO FIND VOLUME WITH WHOLE NUMBERS.

= 8 × 3 × 3·5 cm³

= 84 cm³

5. Find the volume of each of the cuboids.

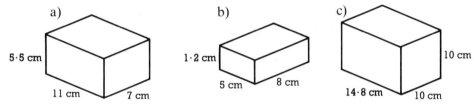

a)

5·5 cm

11 cm   7 cm

b)

1·2 cm

5 cm   8 cm

c)

10 cm

14·8 cm   10 cm

d) Which cuboid has the biggest volume?

6. Find the volume, using the new method, of the cuboid in Question 4.

Does your new answer agree with the answer to Question 4(e)?

7. a) Estimate, in metres, the height of the room you are in.
   b) Estimate the length and the width of the room.
   c) Estimate the volume of the room.

PRISMS

Prisms are solids which are the same all the way through, like a Toblerone pack or an unsharpened pencil.

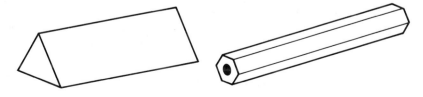

EXERCISE 23c 1. Look at the solids in these drawings.

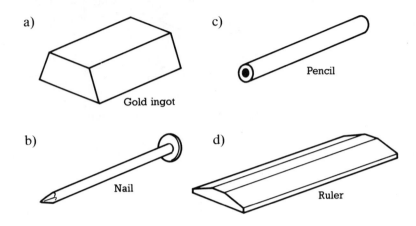

a)

Gold ingot

b)

Nail

c)

Pencil

d)

Ruler

All but one are prisms.

Which object is the odd one out? What made you decide it was different from the others?

2. Which of the following objects are prisms?

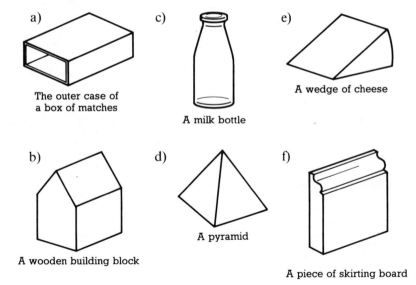

a)

The outer case of
a box of matches

b)

A wooden building block

c)

A milk bottle

d)

A pyramid

e)

A wedge of cheese

f)

A piece of skirting board

3. Name some other objects which are prisms.

4. Below are some objects built out of 1 cm cubes. Some are prisms and some are not.

Name the ones which are prisms.

a) 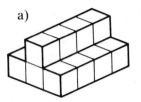   b) 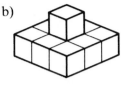   c)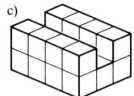

d) 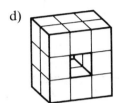   e) 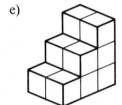   f)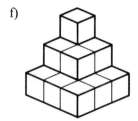

5. This is a triangular prism, and below is a net for it.

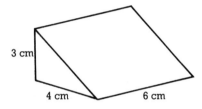

3 cm

4 cm   6 cm

a) Draw the net on 1 cm squared paper and make the prism.

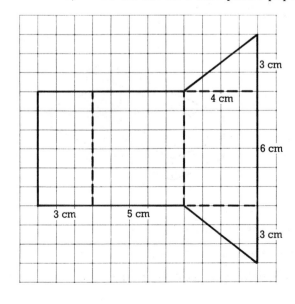

3 cm

4 cm

6 cm

3 cm   5 cm

3 cm

b) How many faces does it have?

c) How many edges does it have?

6. This is a net of a different triangular prism.

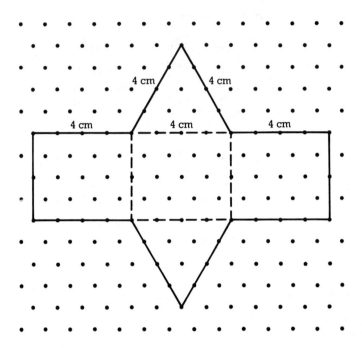

a) Draw it on 1 cm triangular dotted paper and make it up.

b) Does it have the same number of faces, edges and corners as the prism in Question 4?

7.

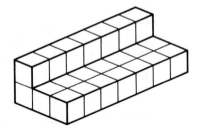

This prism is built out of 1 cm cubes.

a) How many cubes are used to build it?

b) What is the volume of the prism?

8.

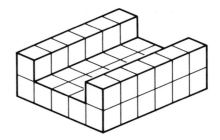

This prism is built out of 1 cm cubes. What is its volume?

9. Find the volume of each of the solids in Question 4.

PYRAMIDS

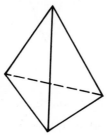 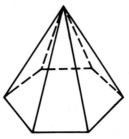

A pyramid has a flat base which can have any number of sides. The other faces are all triangles and they meet at a point.

EXERCISE 23d

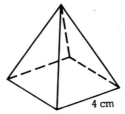

4 cm

1. This is a picture of a pyramid with a square as its base. It is called a square-based pyramid.

Below is a net for this pyramid.

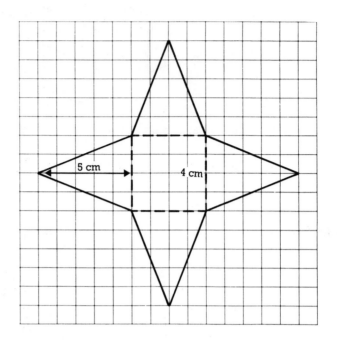

a) Draw the net full size and make the pyramid.

b) How many edges does it have?

c) What is the shape of its base?

d) How many faces does it have?

e) How many corners does it have?

2.

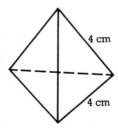

This solid is a triangular-based pyramid.
(The mathematical name is a *tetrahedron*.)

You will need triangular dotted paper to draw the net.

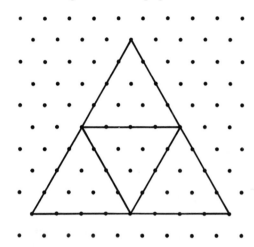

a) Draw the net and make the pyramid.
b) How many faces, edges and corners does it have?

PLANES OF SYMMETRY

EXERCISE 23e 1.

Imagine a chair sliced down the middle.
Put the cut side of one of the halves against a mirror.
Do you see a complete chair?

Looking at the half-chair and its reflection, the plane of the mirror is a *plane of symmetry* of the chair.
(Think of flat drawings and *lines of symmetry*.)

2.

Imagine the chair cut into two pieces in a different way.

a) Put one of the pieces against a mirror.
   Do you see a complete chair?
b) Is the mirror a plane of symmetry this time?
c) Is there any other way of cutting the chair into two pieces so that we can see a complete chair when we put one piece against the mirror?

3.

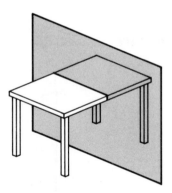

The stool above is cut into two pieces. Is the grey plane a plane of symmetry of the stool?

4. Which of the following objects have a plane of symmetry?

a)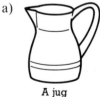

A jug

b)

A clock

c)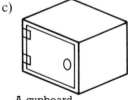

A cupboard

d) Name three other objects which have planes of symmetry.

5. Some objects have a plane of approximate symmetry.
For example, a person's head or a toy car sometimes have rough symmetry if you don't look too closely at the detail.

a) Which of the following objects have rough symmetry?
   A daisy, a book, a real car.
b) Name three other objects which have rough symmetry.
c) Name three objects which do not have even rough symmetry.
d) Why does a bicycle not have a plane of symmetry?

6. Look at the solids in Exercise 23c, Question 4.
a) Which of them has a plane of symmetry?
b) A solid can have more than one plane of symmetry. Which of these solids have more than one?

24 <u>WORKING WITH UNITS</u>

COMMON METRIC UNITS

The units that are usually used for measuring length are kilometres, metres, centimetres and millimetres; and the relationships between them are

> 10 mm = 1 cm
>
> 100 cm = 1 m
>
> 1000 m = 1 km

The common units for measuring weight are the gram and the kilogram. For very heavy objects, the tonne (t) is also used. The relationships between these units are

> 1000 g = 1 kg
>
> 1000 kg = 1 tonne

There is one other unit of weight that you will see on medicines: this is the milligram (mg). There are 1000 mg in one gram so only *very* small quantities are weighed in milligrams.

In Book 1B we saw that when we need to change from a large unit to a smaller unit, we multiply. For example, to give 2 m in cm, we multiply 2 by 100 cm.

EXERCISE 24a 1. Which unit would you choose to use for
  a) the length of your bedroom
  b) the weight of a sack of potatoes
  c) the distance from Exeter to Bristol
  d) the weight of a lorry loaded with bricks
  e) the length of your fingernail
  f) the weight of one egg
  g) the weight of pure aspirin in one pill
  h) the width of a dining table?

Raz cut off 1·2 m of ribbon and Jim cut off 45 cm. How much did they cut off altogether?

BOTH LENGTHS MUST BE IN THE SAME UNIT BEFORE THEY CAN BE ADDED, SO FIRST CHANGE 1·2 m TO CENTIMETRES.

$1·2 \text{ m} = 1·2 \times 100 \text{ cm}$

$= 120 \text{ cm}$

$120 + 45 = 165$

So 165 cm was cut off.

2. Express the given quantity in the unit in brackets.

a) 25 cm   (mm)   c) 1·4 tonnes (kg)   e) 1·6 m   (cm)
b) 1·3 kg (g)   d) 1·5 km (m)   f) 2·5 tonnes (kg)

3. Find the perimeter of each shape.

a)

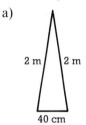

2 m   2 m

40 cm

b)

5 cm

5 cm   4·5 cm

5 mm
5 mm

4·5 cm

c)

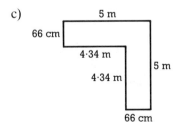

5 m

66 cm

4·34 m

5 m

4·34 m

66 cm

d)

59 mm

4·1 cm

3 cm

4. Sarah had 5 m of copper wire. She cut off 85 cm. Simon then cut off 1·3 m. How much did they cut off altogether?
How much remained?

CHANGING FROM A SMALL UNIT TO A LARGER UNIT

A metre is longer than a centimetre, so there are *fewer* metres than centimetres in a given length. This means that when we change 450 cm to metres, we *divide* by 100.

Whenever we change from a small unit to a large one, we divide.

EXERCISE 24b

Change 450 cm to metres.

$$450 \text{ cm} = 450 \div 100 \text{ m}$$
$$= 4 \cdot 5 \text{ m}$$

1. Express the given quantity in the unit in brackets.

a) 300 mm (cm)   b) 2000 m (km)   c) 250 cm (m)

2. A table is 200 cm long. How many metres is this?

3. Find the perimeter of this triangle in metres.

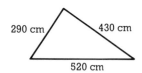

4. Give the quantity in the unit in brackets.

a) 2000 g (kg)   b) 4000 kg (t)   c) 3500 g (kg)

5. Find the total weight of these jars of jam in

a) grams   b) kilograms.

6. The weight of each parcel is written on it.
What is the total weight in

a) grams   b) kilograms?

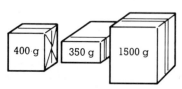

USING UNITS

In some problems, we have to change from large units to smaller ones. There are *more* smaller units than larger units in a given quantity so when changing to smaller units, we *multiply*.
When we have to change to a larger unit, we *divide*.

EXERCISE 24c **1.** a) Find the perimeter of this carpet in metres.

b) Is 10 m of carpet edging enough to go all round the edge of this carpet?

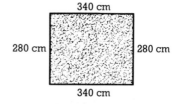

2. a) What is the total weight of these groceries?

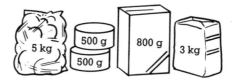

b) Alan reckons that he can carry 15 kg of shopping. Will he be able to carry this load?

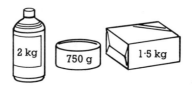

3. One tin of baked beans weighs 220 g. Fifty of these tins fill a box.
What weight, in kilograms, should be written on the box?

4. One fence post is 130 cm long. What length of wood, in metres, is needed to make ten of these posts?

5. A lorry is loaded with bricks. The weight of the bricks is 2·5 tonnes. The weight of the lorry when empty is 2500 kg.
What is the weight of the loaded lorry?

6. A full sack of potatoes weighs 14 kg. Two people each help themselves to 700 g of potatoes.
What is the weight of the potatoes left in the sack?

7.

Which of these vehicles can go under a bridge with this sign on it?

8. Each side of a square is 45 cm long. What is the perimeter of the square in metres?

9. There is a limit of 1 tonne on the weight a lift can carry. If an average adult weighs 70 kg, can the lift carry 20 adults?

10. A girl's journey to school starts with a walk of 500 m to the bus stop. She then travels 2·5 km by bus and still has a walk of 100 m to school.
What distance in metres does the girl have to travel?

IMPERIAL UNITS

In the United Kingdom, all quantities used to be measured in *imperial units*.

Some imperial units are still used. For example, road signs give distances in miles and some food items are still weighed in pounds and ounces.

The common imperial units of *length* are miles, feet (ft) and inches (in).

The common imperial units of *weight* are pounds (lb) and ounces (oz).

Because we are changing from the imperial system of units to the metric system, we have to cope with a mixture of the two sets. This is easier if we can make rough conversions from one set of units to the other set.

WEIGHT

1 kg is about 2 lb   so   1 lb is about 500 g

LENGTH

1 km is about half a mile   so   1 mile is about 2 km

10 cm is about 4 inches

EXERCISE 24d

My recipe book says that I need 6 pounds of sugar to make some jam. Will a 4 kg bag of sugar be enough?

$$1 \text{ kg} \approx 2 \text{ lb}$$
$$4 \text{ kg} \approx 8 \text{ lb}$$

So 4 kg is enough.

1. Give the *rough value* of the given quantity in the unit in brackets.

a) 10 miles (km)   d) 20 inches (cm) g) 6 lb (kg)

b) 30 km (miles)   e) 3 kg (lb)   h) 14 inches (cm)

c) 80 cm (inches) f) 1500 kg (lb)   i) 150 km (miles)

2. This is a diagram from an old maths text book.

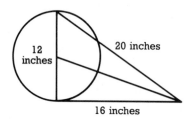

Copy the diagram but give the measurements in centimetres, using 10 cm ≈ 4 inches.

3. What, roughly, is the weight in kilograms of this load of shopping?

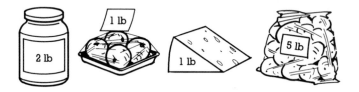

4. Give the rough value of the quantity in the unit in brackets.
   a) 500 g (lb)   b) 8 km (miles)   c) 40 cm (inches)

5. A bag of flour weighs 1·5 kg.
   Roughly how many pounds is this?

6. A road sign in France says that it is 500 km to Paris.
   Roughly how many miles is this?

7. Some old floor tiles are 12 inches square.
   Roughly how many centimetres is the length of one side of a tile?

8. Which is heavier, a 3 kg bag of sugar or a 5 lb bag of potatoes?

9. The instructions for repotting a plant say that it should go in a 10 cm pot. Tom has a 3 inch, a 4 inch and a 5 inch pot. Which one should he use?

10. In one catalogue a table is shown as 70 inches long. In another catalogue a different table is shown as 250 cm long. Which table is longer?

11. A 6-inch-wide floorboard needs replacing. Floorboards are sold in the following widths: 12 cm, 15 cm, 18 cm. Which width is nearest to 6 inches?

12. This is an old imperial screw.

Which of these metric screws is nearest in length to the imperial screw?

UNITS OF LENGTH, AREA AND VOLUME

We can tell from the unit used what kind of quantity is being measured. If we see 5 kg we know that it is a weight.

It is not quite so easy with length, area and volume, as these all involve units of length, but used in different ways.

A length of 6 centimetres is written as 6 cm

An area of 6 square centimetres is written as 6 cm^2

A volume of 6 cubic centimetres is written as 6 cm^3

A little more thought is needed in these cases.

EXERCISE 24e

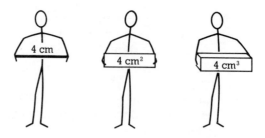

Some of the following quantities are lengths (L), some are areas (A), and some are volumes (V).

Write down L, A or V for each one.

1. 10 cm

2. 21 cm^3

3. 85 m^2

4. 4 m^3

5. 630 mm

6. 75 km^2

7. 6 mm^3

8. 93 km^2

9. 45 cm

10. 8 m^3

11. 923 mm

12. 9 m

13. 17 mm^3

14. 5 mm^2

15. 89 cm^3

25 EQUATIONS

MISSING NUMBERS

EXERCISE 25a Copy each of the following calculations, filling in the missing number.

1. $9 + \boxed{} = 14$ **3.** $4 \times ? = 8$ **5.** $9 = \boxed{} + 2$

2. $? + 3 = 6$ **4.** $\boxed{} - 3 = 2$ **6.** $9 - ? = 5$

Write down the missing number in each of the following sentences.

7. Andy bought a cola costing 35 p and gave _____ p to the shopkeeper. His change was 15 p.

8. A pile of six exercise books is _____ mm thick. Each book is 8 mm thick.

9.

This unstretched curtain wire is _____ cm long. If I can stretch it just 3 cm, it will reach between the two hooks, which are 58 cm apart.

10. I think of a number and add 11. The result is 30. What is the original number?

11. Philip thought of a number, doubled it and added 6. The result was 12. What was Philip's first number?

Find the number that the letter stands for if $4 + c = 7$

$$4 + c = 7$$

| 4 + 3 = 7, SO c MUST BE 3. |

$$c = 3$$

In Questions 12 to 19, write down the number that the letter stands for.

12. $7 + d = 10$ **15.** $g - 5 = 8$

13. $e - 3 = 5$ **16.** $h + 6 = 7$

14. $9 - f = 2$ **17.** $4 = k + 1$

Remember that $3a$ means $3 \times a$

18. $2x = 6$ **19.** $4y = 8$

EQUATIONS

$4 + x = 7$ is called an *equation* because

the left-hand side	is equal to	the right-hand side
$4 + x$	=	7

$4 + x$ on its own is *not* an equation.

EXERCISE 25b 1. Which of these are equations?

     a) $5 - x$ c) $2f = 4$ e) $4x$
     b) $9 = a + 7$ d) $t + 8 = 10$ f) $g + x + 3$

2. Is $4 + x = 12$ an equation? If it is, find the number that x stands for.

3. Is $x - 2$ an equation? If it is, find the number that x stands for.

SOLVING AN EQUATION

When we find what number the letter in an equation stands for, we are *solving* the equation.

If the equation is $x + 2 = 6$, then $x = 4$ is the *solution* of the equation.

EXERCISE 25c

Solve the equation $6 - x = 2$

$$6 - x = 2$$
$$x = 4$$

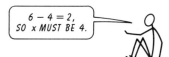

6 − 4 = 2,
SO x MUST BE 4.

Solve the following equations.

1. $a + 6 = 9$ **6.** $4x = 4$

2. $7 - y = 1$ **7.** $z - 2 = 4$

3. $5 + c = 8$ **8.** $8 = t + 3$

4. $3y = 6$ **9.** $9 - x = 5$

5. $9 = x + 2$ **10.** $c + 4 = 8$

Solve the equation $3x + 4 = 10$ by trial and improvement.

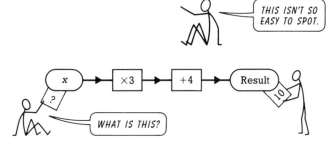

THIS ISN'T SO
EASY TO SPOT.

x   ×3   +4   Result

?

WHAT IS THIS?

Try 3: $3x + 4 = 9 + 4 = 13$ Too large

Try 2: $3x + 4 = 6 + 4 = 10$ This fits

So $x = 2$

Solve the following equations by trial and improvement.

11. $2x + 1 = 9$ **16.** $4 + 2x = 8$

12. $4c - 2 = 6$ **17.** $3y - 1 = 8$

13. $6 - 2x = 4$ **18.** $4 = 1 + 3s$

14. $2a + 3 = 13$ **19.** $4x - 2 = 10$

15. $6 + 3x = 6$ **20.** $5 = 2x + 1$

Solving equations by trial and improvement is not very satisfactory. It can take a long time.

It is better to use a more organised method.

USING A BALANCE TO SOLVE EQUATIONS

Equations can be represented on a balance. For example, suppose we have a bag with an unknown number of 10 p coins in it. (We can say there are x coins in the bag).

We find we can balance the bag and 4 coins against 10 coins.

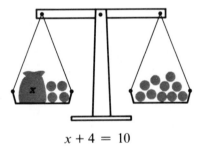

$$x + 4 = 10$$

If we take 4 loose coins from each side we have

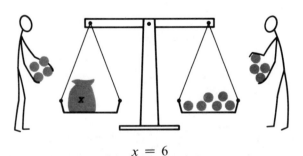

$$x = 6$$

EXERCISE 25d

A bag contains some 10 p coins. The bag and 5 more coins will balance 8 coins.
Draw a balance to show this, and then write an equation.

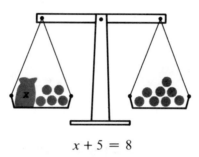

$$x + 5 = 8$$

For Questions 1–3, draw a balance and write an equation as in the worked example.

1. The bag and 2 more coins balance 6 coins.

2. The bag and 4 more coins balance 9 coins.

3. The bag and 1 more coin balance 4 coins.

a) Write an equation for this balance.

b) Make a change to both pans, leaving just the bag in the left pan. If the scales still balance, write down what you have done to each side.

a) $x + 3 = 7$

b) Take 3 coins from each side

$$x = 4$$

In each question, write an equation for the balance.

Then write down what has to be done to make the scales still balance with just the bag in one pan.

4.

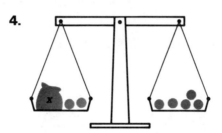

5.

6.

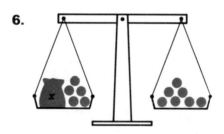

Solve the equation $a + 5 = 8$

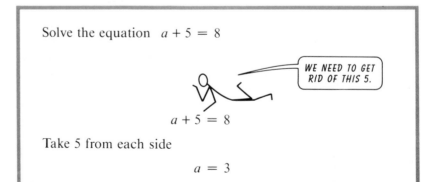

WE NEED TO GET RID OF THIS 5.

$$a + 5 = 8$$

Take 5 from each side

$$a = 3$$

Solve the following equations. In each case, say what you are doing to each side, as in the worked example.

7. $x + 3 = 4$ **10.** $b + 5 = 10$

8. $y + 6 = 9$ **11.** $c + 1 = 6$

9. $z + 2 = 8$ **12.** $d + 8 = 8$

EQUATIONS WITH A MINUS SIGN

With the equation $x + 3 = 2$, where 3 is *added* to x, we *subtracted* 3 from each side to get rid of the 3.

In the equation $x - 4 = 5$, the 4 is being *subtracted*.
To get rid of it we *add* 4 to each side.

EXERCISE 25e

Solve the equation $x - 3 = 4$

WE ARE SHORT OF 3 ON THE LEFT, SO WE ADD.

$x - 3 = 4$

Add 3 to each side

$x = 7$

Solve the following equations. In each case, say what you are doing to each side.

1. $x - 6 = 8$ **4.** $y - 3 = 6$

2. $a - 3 = 4$ **5.** $z - 1 = 8$

3. $c - 2 = 5$ **6.** $b - 4 = 1$

EQUATIONS WITH MULTIPLES OF *X*

We want to solve the equation $3x = 6$

REMEMBER THAT 3x MEANS $3 \times x$.

We can think of $3x$ as 3 bags each containing x coins.

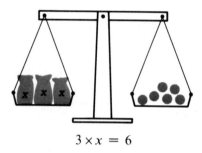

$$3 \times x = 6$$

Divide both sides by 3.

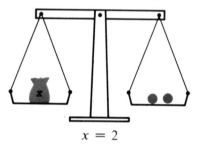

$$x = 2$$

EXERCISE 25f

Solve the equation $4x = 8$

$$4x = 8$$

WE HAVE FOUR x'S AND WE ONLY WANT ONE.

Divide both sides by 4

$$x = 2$$

Solve the following equations. Say what you are doing to each side.

1. $2x = 8$	**3.** $5x = 15$	**5.** $6c = 12$
2. $4z = 8$	**4.** $3z = 9$	**6.** $2x = 0$

MIXED EQUATIONS

EXERCISE 25g Solve the following equations, saying in each case what you are doing to each side.

1. $x + 4 = 7$	**6.** $4s = 8$	**11.** $2x = 12$
2. $x - 2 = 3$	**7.** $4 + s = 8$	**12.** $x + 2 = 2$
3. $3x = 6$	**8.** $s + 4 = 8$	**13.** $y - 5 = 5$
4. $a - 5 = 2$	**9.** $s - 4 = 8$	**14.** $3y = 3$
5. $c + 7 = 11$	**10.** $c - 7 = 1$	**15.** $5 + z = 9$

USING THE NEW METHOD

The equations in the last few exercises *could* be done by guesswork. Now we come to equations which have awkward solutions and which are difficult to solve by guesswork.

EXERCISE 25h

Solve the equation $5x = 12$

$$5x = 12$$

Divide both sides by 5

$$x = 12 \div 5$$
$$= 2{\cdot}4$$

REMEMBER, WHATEVER YOU DO TO ONE SIDE, YOU MUST ALSO DO TO THE OTHER.

Solve the following equations. Use a calculator if necessary.

1. $x + 5{\cdot}5 = 8$	**3.** $4z = 7$	**5.** $4 + y = 5{\cdot}7$
2. $a - 3 = 2{\cdot}4$	**4.** $c + 2 = 3{\cdot}4$	**6.** $y - 2{\cdot}5 = 3$

7. $2x = 9$ **10.** $z - 3 = 6{\cdot}9$ **13.** $s - 1{\cdot}3 = 2{\cdot}5$

8. $b + 6 = 7{\cdot}2$ **11.** $t + 4{\cdot}6 = 8$ **14.** $2a = 9{\cdot}2$

9. $5x = 13$ **12.** $5x = 7$ **15.** $p - 1{\cdot}6 = 4{\cdot}9$

26 SCALE DRAWING

A scale drawing is a smaller drawing of an original object.

If 1 centimetre on the drawing represents 1 metre on the actual object this is the *scale* of the drawing.

We can write this as 1 cm ≡ 1 m.

The scale must always be written on a scale drawing.

EXERCISE 26a

This is a scale drawing of Jenny's lounge.

Scale: 1 cm ≡ 1 m

a) How long, in centimetres, is this drawing of the lounge?

b) How long is the actual lounge?

c) How wide, in centimetres, is this drawing of the lounge?

d) How wide is the actual lounge?

USE A RULER TO MEASURE THE SIDES.

a) The lounge is 4·5 cm long in the drawing.

b) The actual length of the lounge is 4·5 m.

c) The lounge is 3 cm wide in the drawing.

b) The actual width of the lounge is 3 m.

1 cm REPRESENTS 1 m.

1. This is a scale drawing of Len's living room.

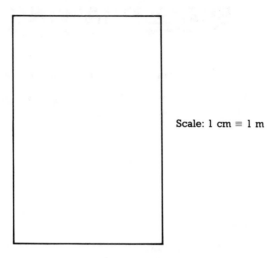

Scale: 1 cm ≡ 1 m

a) How long, in centimetres, is this diagram of the living room?
b) How long is the actual living room?
c) How wide, in centimetres, is the drawing of the living room?
d) How wide is the actual living room?

2. This is a plan of Jane's lounge.

Scale: 1 cm ≡ 1 m

a) How long, in centimetres, is this plan?
b) How wide, in centimetres, is this plan at the widest point?
c) How long is the actual lounge?
d) How wide is the actual lounge?
e) What is the perimeter of the lounge, in centimetres?
f) What is the perimeter of the lounge, in metres?

3. The main English classroom is a rectangle measuring 12 m by 8 m.

   a) Use a scale in which 1 cm represents 1 metre, to draw a plan of this room.

   b) On the plan, what is the distance between opposite corners?

   c) How far apart are the opposite corners of the room?

4. This is a scale drawing of a plot of land.

Scale: 1 cm ≡ 2 metres

   a) How long, in centimetres, is this scale drawing?

   b) How long, in metres, is the plot of land?

   c) What is the distance, in centimetres, between opposite corners of the scale drawing?

   d) What is the distance, in metres, between opposite corners of the plot of land?

5. Pete drew a plan of a classroom. Unfortunately he forgot to put on the scale. The actual length of the room is 8 metres.

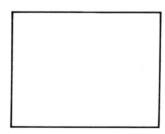

   a) What scale did he use?

   b) How wide is the classroom?

6. This is a scale drawing of the ground floor plan of a house.

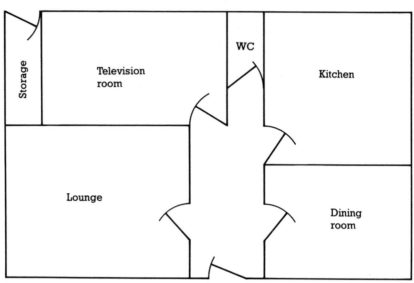

Scale: 1 cm ≡ 1 metre

Using a ruler, take measurements from the drawing to answer the following questions about the actual house.

a) How long is the lounge?

b) How wide is the dining room?

c) How long is the TV room?

d) What is the perimeter of the kitchen?

What is the size of the house

e) from end to end   f) from back to front?

7. The plan on page 259 shows the first floor of a science block. The side of each square represents 1 metre. Use this plan to find

a) the length of the biology laboratory

b) the width of the biology laboratory

c) the length and breadth of classroom A

d) the length and breadth of classroom D

e) the perimeter of classroom C

f) which room has two entrances from the corridor

g) which rooms have no direct entrance from the corridor

h) the length and breadth of the corridor

i) the length and breadth of the first floor of the science block

j) the perimeter of the smallest room on the floor.

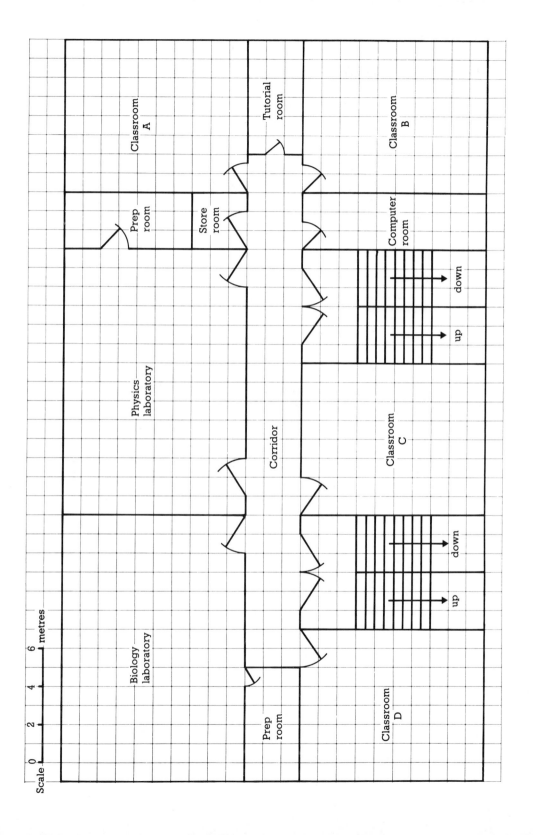

INFORMATION FROM MAPS

Maps are scale drawings of areas of land.

EXERCISE 26b

This map shows part of the south-east of England. Find the straight-line distance between London and Dover.

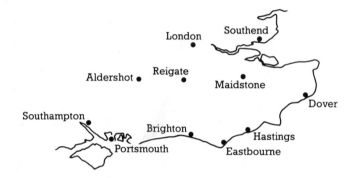

Scale: 1 cm represents 20 miles.

MEASURING FROM THE MAP, THE STRAIGHT-LINE DISTANCE BETWEEN LONDON AND DOVER IS 3·3 cm.

1 cm represents 20 miles

3·3 cm represents 3·3 × 20 miles = 66 miles

The distance between London and Dover is 66 miles.

1. Use the map in the worked example to find the distance between
    a) London and Brighton
    b) Southampton and Dover
    c) Southend and Portsmouth
    d) Reigate and Hastings.

2.

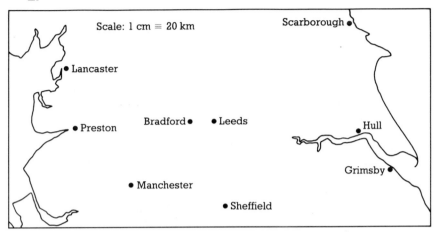

The scale on this map is 1 cm to 20 kilometres. Use the map to find the distance between

a) Manchester and Hull   c) Preston and Grimsby
b) Scarborough and Leeds   d) Sheffield and Bradford.

3.

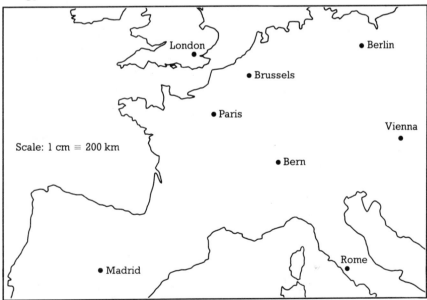

The scale on this map is 1 cm to 200 kilometres. Use the map to find the distance between

a) London and Paris   c) Rome and Berlin
b) London and Rome   d) Madrid and Vienna.

4.

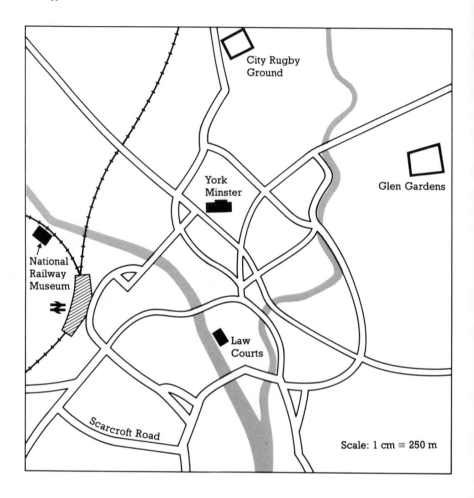

The scale on this street map of York is 1 cm to 250 m. Use the map to find the straight line distance

a) between York Minster and Glen Gardens

b) between the National Railway Museum and City Rugby Ground

c) between the two ends of Scarcroft Road

d) from the National Railway Museum by river to the Law Courts

e) from the Law Courts to York Minster.

5.

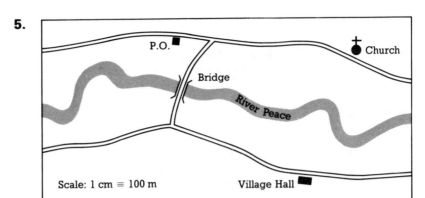

The map shows the village of Gottam.

a) How far is it in a straight line from the church to the village hall?

b) How far is it from the church to the village hall using the bridge?

27 NETWORKS

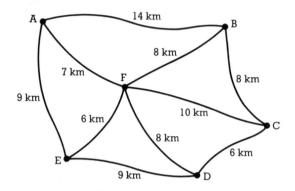

This road map shows distances between villages.

a) How far is it from A to B?
b) How far is it from A to C via F?
c) What is the distance from A to C if you go via B?
d) Find the distance from A to C via F and D.
e) Find another possible route from A to C and give the distance.
f) Which is the shortest route from A to C?

This is the map of a village showing some of the buildings and the distances between them.

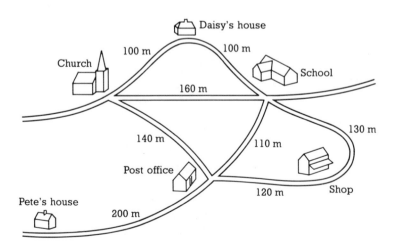

264

2. a) Pete decided to walk from his home to Daisy's house. He went past the post office, the shop and the school.
How far did he walk?

    b) At the same time, Daisy set off to visit Pete. She went past the church and the post office to Pete's house.
How far did she walk?

    c) Pete and Daisy missed each other. They both set off to walk back and met halfway between the post office and the school.
How far had Pete walked altogether?

3. On another day, Pete and Daisy set off from Pete's house and walked past the post office, the church, Daisy's house, the school and the shop and back to the post office.

    a) How far did they walk?

    b) Is there any section of road they did not walk along?

4. a) On Monday, the postman collects the post from the post office as usual.

       He finds that he has letters to deliver to the school, the shop and Daisy's house, before returning to the post office.

       Plan a route for him so that he walks as short a distance as possible. Give the distance he walks.

    b) On Tuesday, the postman has letters for Daisy and Pete. Plan his route for him and give the distance.

5.

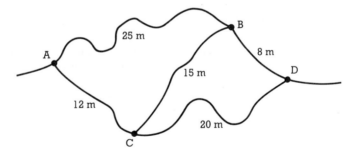

This road map shows the distances between towns in miles.

a) How far is it from A to C?

b) How far is it from A to D via B?

c) How far is it from A to D if you call at B and then C on the way?

d) Find the shortest route from A to D.

e) What is the next shortest route from A to D?

6.

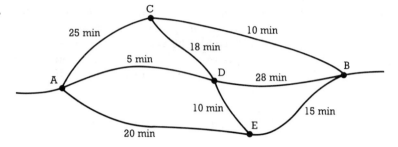

This road map shows the times it takes to cycle along the various roads.

a) How long does it take to go from C to B?

b) How long does it take to go from A to B via E?

c) Find a quicker route for getting from A to B.

d) Find the quickest route from B to D.

e) Find the quickest route from E to C.

NETWORKS

All the diagrams in the last exercise are *networks* showing connections between places.

If we are interested in, say, distances only and not in how wiggly the road is, we can draw a simplified version.

The map in Question 5 on page 265 can be redrawn more simply.

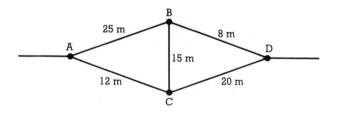

Notice that the lengths are not drawn to scale.

EXERCISE 27b

Draw a simplified version of the given road network.

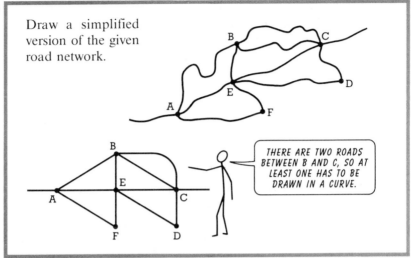

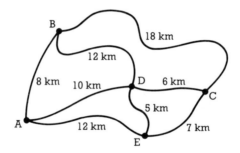

THERE ARE TWO ROADS BETWEEN B AND C, SO AT LEAST ONE HAS TO BE DRAWN IN A CURVE.

1.

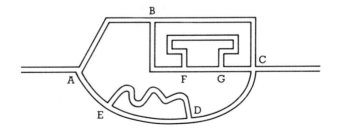

This map shows the distances between villages. Draw a simplified network and mark in the distances.

2.

This is the map of a village. Draw a simplified network, using a single line to represent a road.

3. Draw a simplified network to represent Pete and Daisy's village in Question 2 of the previous exercise.

4.

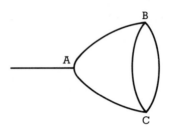

This is a simplified network showing the roads linking three points A, B and C.

A, B and C in fact lie in one straight line.

$$\overset{\bullet}{\text{A}} \qquad\qquad \overset{\bullet}{\text{B}} \qquad\qquad \overset{\bullet}{\text{C}}$$

Draw a road map showing the roads as they might possibly be in reality. (The roads might curve or bend.)

DRAWING NETWORKS

Some networks can be drawn in one go, i.e. without lifting pen from paper and without going over any line again.

EXERCISE 27c 1. Copy the diagram without lifting pen or pencil from the paper and without going over any line again.
Start at A.

Try starting at B. Is the drawing still possible?
Now try starting at C.

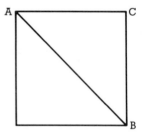

2. Draw each of the following diagrams in the same way as in Question 1.
Start each one at the point labelled A.

a)   b)    c)

3. It is not possible to draw at least one of the following diagrams without lifting your pen from the paper or going over a line again.

Find which can be drawn in this way and which cannot.

a) 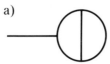 b) 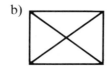 c)

4. The following diagrams can be copied in one go if you choose your starting point carefully.

i) 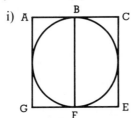   ii)    iii)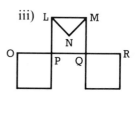

a) Name the points you could start from in order to complete a drawing in one go.

b) Name starting points that do *not* allow you to do the drawing in one go.

5. Make a network drawing of your own showing some of the roads near the school or near where you live.

Can your network be drawn without lifting pen from paper?

MIXED EXERCISE

EXERCISE 27d 1.

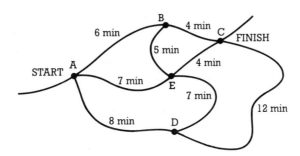

This map shows the time it takes to travel from point to point.

a) Find the quickest route from start to finish and give the time taken.

b) Find the slowest route from start to finish without travelling along any road twice. Give the time it takes.

2. This drawing shows part of a board game, marked with circles and lines.

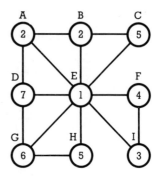

There is a pile of counters on each circle; for example, there are 7 on D and 4 on F.

Move from A to I along the lines, on the way picking up as many counters as possible from the circles you pass through.

You may not pass through a circle which has no counters left. An example is ABCEI which gives $2 + 2 + 5 + 1 + 3$, i.e. 13 counters.

a) Describe another route from A to I by giving the letters of the circles you pass through. How many counters have you collected this time?

b) Find the route that gives the most counters.

3.

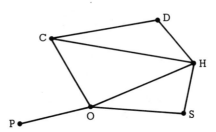

This is a simplified version of the map of Pete and Daisy's village.

a) Can the diagram be drawn in one go? Try starting first from D, then from P.

Try other starting points. Write down what you find out.

b) The postman, starting from O, has letters for C, D, H, P and S.

Can he deliver the letters and return to O without walking along any bit of road twice?

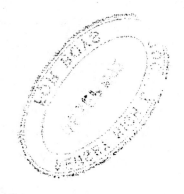